CW00323439

MORETON HALL
* 0 0 0 0 9 1 2 8 *

THE FIRES WITHIN

VOLCANOES ON EARTH AND OTHER PLANETS

THE FIRES WITHIN

VOLCANOES ON EARTH AND OTHER PLANETS

ILLUSTRATED BY
DAVID A. HARDY

WRITTEN BY
JOHN MURRAY

DEDICATION

In memory of Maurice and Katia Krafft and Harry Glicken, who lost their lives on Mount Unzen, Japan, during the writing of this book.

Dragon's World Ltd
Limpsfield
Surrey RH8 0DY
Great Britain

First published by Dragon's World 1991

Editor: Patricia Burgess
Designer: Tom Deas
Art Director: David Hardy
Editorial Director: Pippa Rubinstein

The catalogue record for this book is available from the British Library

ISBN 1 85028 123 8

Typeset by Flairplan Phototypesetting Ltd.

Printed in Portugal

CONTENTS

FOREWORD

Humans have lived with volcanoes ever since a creature that could be called human first walked the face of the Earth. For aeons volcanic activity was something to be avoided, since at the very least it was both frightening and inexplicable, and at worst brought death and destruction.

As civilization began to mature, volcanoes were worshipped as deities, along with other awesome natural phenomena like the Sun, Moon, thunder and lightning. It is only very recently – a mere tick of the geological clock – that volcanoes have become a subject of inspiration for writers, poets and artists, and a subject for research by scientists.

During the last three decades of the nineteenth century, artists of what has become known as the 'Hudson River School', including Thomas Moran and Albert Bierstadt, painted scenes in the western USA which, though romanticized, made the public aware of natural wonders such as the Grand Canyon, Yellowstone's thermal areas and the scenic Yosemite Valley, leading to the formation of national parks. A century earlier, in Europe, Joseph Wright of Derby forsook pastoral landscapes for spectacular subjects, producing such paintings as 'Eruption of Vesuvius' (1774). These artists are now seen as the direct forebears of today's astronomical or 'space artists' among whom David Hardy is numbered.

Today's space artists, armed with knowledge derived from space probes such as *Viking*, *Venera* and *Voyager*, which, in the 1970s and 1980s, first revealed volcanoes on other bodies in the solar system, visit remote, weird and usually volcanic spots on our own planet, seeking not only inspiration but scientific analogues of landscapes which are to be found on worlds like Mars, Venus, Io and Triton. (It is, after all, impossible – as yet – for them to visit the worlds they paint!) To this end, Hardy has twice visited Iceland, where there are shield volcanoes, thermal areas and fault valleys like those on Mars, the volcanic islands of Hawaii, and other interesting areas in Italy and Greece. The idea of this book thus came about as a natural progression from these travels and interests. All the illustrations are paintings (many in oils) and wherever possible they are based on sketches or photographs taken by the artist or author. None are slavish copies of photographs that might be found in other books because the artist's imagination has injected new life in the form of different angles and weather conditions, and dramatic lighting.

John Murray is a volcanologist and space scientist (unknown job descriptions at the beginning of this century) who, twenty years ago, began a long-term research programme using geophysical techniques to try to understand and predict Mount Etna in Sicily. He has been involved in numerous other studies, including some involving the Moon, Mars and Mercury, and in this book he shares his often hard-won expertise. While acknowledging the tremendous power of volcanoes and their dramatic impact on both people and environment, he is keen to put them in perspective and present a balanced view – after all, of the fifty or so eruptions that occur in an average year, only two result in any loss of human life.

This book, then, is a collaboration between an artist and a scientist. Both share a fascination with the drama and beauty of volcanoes, coupled with an abiding scientific curiosity. Between them they hope to convey the excitement and variety of volcanoes, in both space and time, as well as imparting a great deal of information about major and minor eruptions, how volcanoes work, and how they may be used and even controlled.

David A. Hardy
John B. Murray
January 1991

Prehistoric eruption.
(Painting from the private collection of Mr & Mrs I. Donald)

1 THE UNQUIET EARTH

Volcanoes are among the most exciting, beautiful, awe-inspiring and powerful manifestations of the forces of nature, and their universal fascination is reflected in language, legends and pictorial records throughout the world. Yet the average person knows little about the workings of volcanoes – how useful they can be and how well they can be predicted – and all too often has a greatly distorted view of their destructive properties. These popular misconceptions can be seen in a number of films where volcanoes play a major part in the drama: real dangers are frequently glossed over and minor ones exaggerated to a remarkably unrealistic degree. Anyone who has witnessed a volcano in full paroxysmal eruption would find such films almost insultingly feeble by comparison.

This book begins with descriptions of three volcanic eruptions which particularly affected people living on and around the volcanoes concerned. The first two are famous, destructive events that shocked the world, while the third is a quieter affair which resulted in no human casualties. Between them, these eruptions show the variety of volcanic phemonena that can be encountered and provide the reader with some important terminology and explanations. (Technical terms are *italicized* usually when first mentioned and explained; subsequent mentions are followed by a page reference to the relevant explanation.)

Volcanic eruptions can be extremely powerful. The largest this century were about 1000 times more powerful than a megaton nuclear weapon, and prehistoric eruptions exceeded even this by many hundreds of times. It is this earth-shattering kind of eruption that sticks in the mind and colours the view of anyone who has not lived near a volcano. Such eruptions, however, are unusual and it is important to remember this fact when considering the whole phenomenon. This is not to diminish the dangers that some volcanoes present, merely to put them in perspective. The three descriptions that follow aim to do just this.

A reconstruction of one of the culminating explosions of the 1883 eruption of Krakatoa, which produced the loudest known sounds on Earth.

KRAKATOA, 1883

The eruption of Krakatoa was not the largest ever recorded, but it must rank as one of the most famous, partly because of its location. The uninhabited island of Krakatoa lay in the middle of the Sunda Straits between Java and Sumatra in Indonesia, one of the world's busiest shipping lanes.

The activity began on 20 May 1883 at 10.30 a.m. with loud detonations and a jet of ash and vapour that rapidly rose to a height of 36,000 ft (11,000 metres). Initially the eruption created much local interest and a steamship company organized an excursion to Krakatoa in the *Loudon*. A party of trippers landed on 27 May and actually climbed to the edge of the active crater Perboewatan, just over ½ mile (1 km) across, and looked in to see ash rising and pumice being thrown up to 600 ft (200 metres) high. The eruption continued for the following three months, but interest soon waned.

Subsequently, on 11 August, a surveying unit sailed to Krakatoa to map the new activity. They found three major craters in activity and no fewer than eleven smaller ones, so the survey was abandoned.

The activity gradually increased until, on 26 August at 5.07 p.m., came an enormous explosion which could be heard 500 miles (800 km) away. This was the first of nine huge explosions that marked the culmination of the eruption.

The eyewitness accounts of people comparatively close to the eruption make exciting reading. At 7 p.m. Controller Beyerinck, stationed at Katimbang on Sumatra, 25 miles (40 km) north of Krakatoa, saw that the sea was rising and falling peculiarly. An hour later the highest waves were approaching the outbuildings of his own home, so he decided to take his wife and three children to safety in the hills. As they were preparing to leave, a roaring noise could be heard approaching and seconds later a giant wave hit the house. This was a *tsunami*, sometimes incorrectly called a tidal wave, the first of many that night and the following day. Luckily the house withstood the shock and the family made good their escape.

Meanwhile, the steamship *Loudon* was on a routine trip to Telok Betong, 50 miles (80 km) north of Krakatoa, where she anchored offshore. Throughout the night the ashfall increased and then pumice began to fall. At daybreak they could see small boats in difficulties near the shore and the steamship *Berouw* had been washed aground. Suddenly, at 7 a.m., a tremendous wave appeared behind the *Loudon*, blocking the view and moving very rapidly. The captain just had time to turn the ship round to head into the wave as it hit them. Although the ship took a colossal tumbling, it survived, but this monstrous wave broke on to the shore and raced inland. Three similar waves followed, which destroyed the entire town of Telok Betong before the passengers' eyes and carried the steamer *Berouw* 1½ miles (2½ km) inland.

Meanwhile, the newly-arrived young telegraph master at Anjer, a coastal town 25 miles (40 km) east of Krakatoa, had an even narrower escape. On the night of 26 August he slept soundly, undisturbed by the series of vast explosions from Krakatoa, which at midnight awakened the residents of Daly Springs, Australia, some 2000 miles (3250 km) distant.

At 5.15 a.m. he was up again and supervising repairs to a broken telegraph line. Happening to look out to sea, he saw an enormous wave in the distance, like a mountain rushing towards him. Shouting a warning to his fellow workers, he turned and ran for his life. The roaring wave followed, knocking to pieces everything in its path. Running as fast as his legs could carry him, he eventually fell in total exhaustion on a hillside and resigned himself to his fate. Looking back, he saw to his amazement that the wave had come within thirty paces of him and was now retreating. He was eventually able to escape inland, one of just a handful of survivors from Anjer; many of those who survived this wave were drowned by the larger ones which followed.

Meanwhile, the Beyerinck family on the Sumatra coast were not so lucky. Leaving their house in Katimbang for a hut on higher ground, they had to wade through flooded paddy fields and thick tropical jungle, all in the pitch dark and with blood-sucking leeches stuck to their skin. Eventually they reached the hut at midnight, where they found about 3000 of the local population had also converged. By 5 a.m. the ashfall was so thick that they could not see the coast. Around them flashes of lightning, St Elmo's fire and other electrical phemomena associated with the eruption lit up the trees with an eerie greenish light. When daylight came they could see that the town of Katimbang had been totally destroyed.

Although they were 25 miles (40 km) from Krakatoa and had managed to escape the tsunamis, they could not escape the effects of the vast culminating explosion at 10.02 a.m. – the greatest of them all and the loudest sound yet known on Earth. From this gigantic event a wall of hot ash made its way inexorably towards them, fountaining up into the room through cracks in the floor. A terrifically heavy pressure threw them to the ground and was immediately followed by the air apparently being sucked away so that they could not breathe. It was only later, when they recovered consciousness and got outside, that they realized they had been badly burned.

Of the 3000 people around their hut, about 1000 died of burns and the Beyerinck's youngest child also died. Only here on Sumatra were people killed by direct volcanic activity in the form of hot ash and pumice; elsewhere it was the waves that killed.

When the ashfall became less severe, the Beyerincks started back down to the coast. This time they had to contend with a rain of hot, heavy mud. At last, late in the afternoon, the light gradually returned and it was possible to see across the Sunda Straits. What had happened to Krakatoa? More than half the main island, about 9 square miles (24 square km), had simply disappeared into the sea and many new smoking islands had appeared to the north of it.

The passengers of the *Loudon* were more fortunate. After seeing the destruction of Telok Betong and realizing that they could be of no assistance, they sailed for Anjer on the morning of 27 August to report what had happened. However, the ash rain got thicker and the sky darker, and when large pumice stones began to fall at 10 a.m., they dropped anchor some 45 miles (70 km) from Krakatoa. By 10.30 a.m. it was darker than the darkest night and the wind increased to the force of a hurricane. Lightning struck the ship several times and St Elmo's fire kept appearing all over the mast and yard-arms. The rain of pumice stones changed to a rain of mud so heavy that in ten minutes it lay 6 in (15 cm) deep on the decks. Several tsunami waves hit the ship, but every so often the sea and winds would calm down, leaving an eerie stillness that in the darkness seemed worse than the storm.

Miraculously the ship managed to withstand the onslaught. After eighteen hours of darkness, the sky finally cleared before dawn on 28 August and the *Loudon* once more started for Anjer. Pumice and ash continued to fall and there was now more than 18 in (45 cm) of mud on the deck. As they approached the straits 25 miles (40 km) north of Krakatoa, it looked as if the way was barred by a new strip of land. On closer inspection however, it became clear that the 'new land' was vast rafts of floating pumice 6–10 ft (2–3 metres) high, covered with driftwood, roofs and even uprooted trees that managed to stand curiously upright.

Drawing within sight of Krakatoa, they saw that most of the island had disappeared and that the new reefs to the north occasionally shot great jets of steam into the air. On nearing the Java coast, they could clearly see that everything had been obliterated up to a well-defined 'high water mark'; below this was a muddy mess of destruction.

Only gradually did a complete picture emerge of this horrific natural disaster. Even in Jakarta, nearly 125 miles (200 km) away, the air pressure of the culminating series of explosions could be felt as a strange pressing sensation in the ears. It also disturbed the pressure in the gasworks sufficiently to extinguish many of the gaslights in the town. After the greatest explosion at 10.02 a.m. on 27 August, the sky over Jakarta had become quite dark by 11 a.m., and the associated tsunami, still over 6 ft (2 metres) high, hit the town at 12.30, destroying much of the canal wall and wrecking many boats.

This vast explosion was heard at Rodriguez Island on the other side of the Indian Ocean, some 3000 miles (4650 km) distant. The airwave caused by it was recorded by every single recording barograph on Earth, some as many as seven times, as the wave travelled to the antipodes (the Caribbean) and back again to Krakatoa for five days after the explosion.

The giant sea waves associated with this explosion reached heights of 130 ft (40 metres) above sea level. At least 36,417 people were killed and 165 coastal towns and villages destroyed. Appalling sights were common in and increasingly far from the Sunda Straits for months afterwards, as ships encountered hundreds of animal carcasses and human corpses drowned in the tsunamis. The sea waves were recorded at tide gauges around the Earth, arriving at Aden, some 3800 miles (6000 km) away about twelve hours later.

Ash fell on ships up to 3860 miles (6070 km) away and the finer dust launched into the atmosphere eventually spread right round the Earth, causing vivid red glows after sunset that were sometimes mistaken for fires; indeed, fire engines were called out in some American cities. These sunsets continued for three years and the atmospheric dust lowered global temperatures by about half a degree in the year following the eruption. Rafts of floating pumice, sometimes thick enough to support people, trees and animals, crossed the Indian Ocean in ten months. Some reached Melanesia and remained afloat for two years.

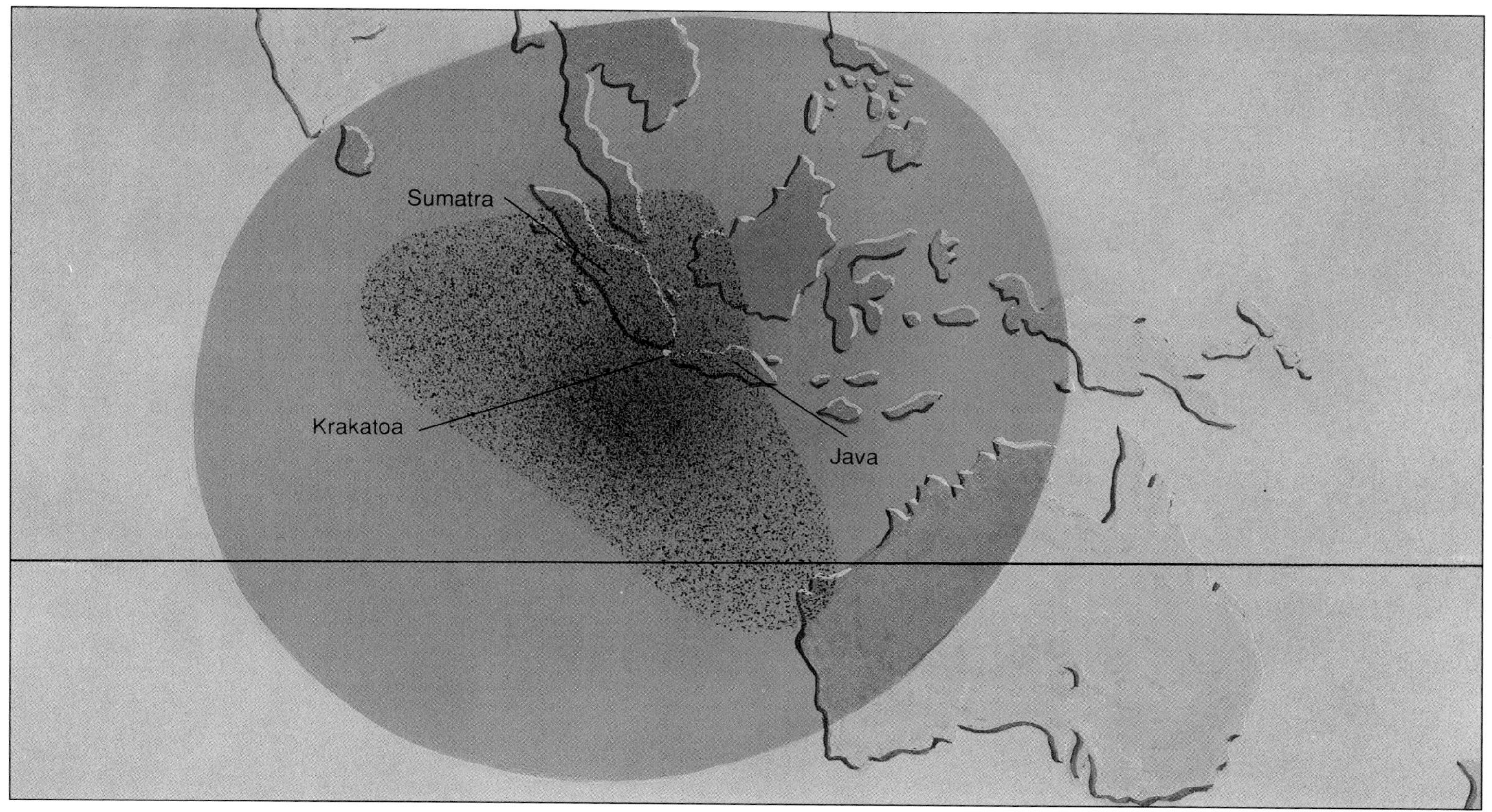

Map of the area around Krakatoa. The stippled region shows where ash fell in 1883, and the larger, almost circular zone indicates the area over which the sound of explosions was heard.

A view of St Pierre, Martinique, with Mount Pelée behind, around eight o'clock on the morning of 8 May 1902. A short while before, a nuée ardente had swept through the city, setting it ablaze and killing all but one of its inhabitants.

The smoking ruins of St Pierre as they appeared to the first people on the scene after the disaster of 8 May 1902.

MOUNT PELÉE, 1902

Unlike Krakatoa in 1883, Mount Pelée in the West Indies was already known to be an active volcano before it sprang into life in April 1902. The first indications that an eruption might be about to happen were noticed by a party of picnickers who climbed the volcano on 23 March from the port of St Pierre, the thriving capital of Martinique, which stood at the southern foot of the volcano about 4 miles (7 km) from the summit. They reported that sulphurous vapours were being emitted from several points near the summit of the mountain on the south side.

It was not until 25 April that the eruption proper began in the same place, with minor explosive activity. This slowly built up over the following week, and in the first few days of May people began to be alarmed. By this time the explosions had considerably increased in strength, some of them being very loud, and volcanic ash fell almost continuously on St Pierre. There was also a strong smell of sulphur and other volcanic gases when the wind blew from the volcano.

The first disaster came on 5 May. The activity on the south side had been building up within a small crater lake, which had now heated up to near boiling point. The gradual infill of new volcanic material was also steadily displacing the water, until suddenly the crater walls gave way and a huge volume of boiling water crashed down the valley of the Rivière Blanche, which enters the sea 1 mile (2 km) north of St Pierre. On the way it mixed with volcanic ash, soil and boulders up to 49 tons (50 tonnes) in weight to form a devastating mud flow travelling at 60 mph (90 kph). Unfortunately, a sugar processing factory lay in its path and thirty men were killed. It then hit the sea with some force, causing tsunami waves which capsized a yacht, drowning all on board, and also flooding some of the shore at St Pierre.

Following this event, people began to leave St Pierre for safer parts of the island, but the authorities were reluctant to mount a full-scale evacuation. This was to save expense and to safeguard the election planned for 10 May. If most people left town, or an evacuation was ordered, the election would have to be postponed, bringing political uncertainty to the small nation.

In view of all these problems, a scientific enquiry was set up, consisting of the most learned scientists on the island. There were no volcanologists among them; indeed, the word 'volcanologist' did not then exist, and certainly no one among those appointed was capable of producing recommendations based on any detailed knowledge of active volcanoes. The report was a classic 'don't panic' document and public figures almost unanimously took up the task of calming the fears of the population. On 7 May the editor of *Les Colonies*, the local newspaper, published an article in which he wrote: 'Where better could one be than at St Pierre? Do those who invade Fort de France [the island's second largest town, on the south coast] imagine that they will be safer should the earth begin to tremble? This would be a foolish conclusion, against which everyone should be warned.' These complacent words appeared in the last issue of *Les Colonies* to be printed.

The following morning, 8 May, at 7.50 a.m., a series of deafening blasts was heard and an enormous black cloud rose from the volcano. The base of the cloud expanded rapidly and slid effortlessly downslope towards St Pierre, spreading out sideways as it did so. In the space of a few minutes, everyone in St Pierre

OVERLEAF: *Lava pouring from two small vents on the upper flanks of Mount Etna.*

was dead, apart from one prisoner in the jail. He was in a cell below ground with only one small air vent. He later reported that everything went dark and scaldingly hot air with ash filled the cell, badly burning his back and legs. Unable to escape, he remained terrified, hungry and thirsty for four days until someone heard his cries for help.

In the centre of town the power of the blast was tremendous. The massive stone walls of the cathedral were swept over, while iron girders and roofs were ripped away and wrapped around obstacles as if made of cloth. In other parts of town there were no signs of such force and entire families were found sitting dead in rooms where crockery and cutlery remained undisturbed as they had been laid out. Although all the bodies showed severe burns, clothes were not usually set alight, suggesting that the intense heat did not last long. However, many fires were started and these raged rapidly through the town, destroying much that had been left standing by the hot cloud. In total about 30,000 people perished.

The hot black cloud of dense ash that swept down to St Pierre like water was then an unknown volcanic phenomenon. Later called a *nuée ardente* (burning cloud) by Albert Lacroix, a geologist from France who came to study the eruption, it consists of a very dense hot mixture of gas, dust and rocks, so compact and mobile that it rolls downhill like water, expanding rapidly as it does so. Many other nuées, large and small, were to follow this first disastrous one; another passed through the town again on 20 May, causing further devastation but claiming no victims.

It is indicative of human resilience in the face of disaster that many people elsewhere around the volcano did not flee, perhaps could not, as their means of livelihood lay close to Mount Pelée. In particular, the town of Morne Rouge, 4 miles (6 km) southeast of the summit, was actually closer to the volcano than St Pierre, but had avoided the 8 May nuée and the others which followed the deep valleys on the southwest slopes of the volcano. Also, many geologists and enthusiasts from all over the world came to observe and climb Mount Pelée in the ensuing months, despite the continued dangers, particularly from nuées ardentes. For example, a party climbed to the top on the afternoon of 30 August. A few hours later, at 9 p.m., another terrible nuée left the crater. This time it swept down the easterly slopes, wiping out many farms and homesteads, and hitting Morne Rouge, where the entire population of 1500 people was killed.

The eruption continued until the following year, but this was the last of the nuées to claim any lives. The accounts of this terrible eruption shocked the world. Despite the smaller scale of devastation, Mount Pelée seemed perhaps more frightful than Krakatoa 20 years before because it was a modern, thriving city that suffered total devastation.

MOUNT ETNA, 1971

While such eruptions as Krakatoa hit the headlines and appal the world by the amount of death and destruction they cause, most volcanic eruptions cause no casualties and never become known to anyone except volcanologists and those who happen to live nearby.

Mount Etna on the island of Sicily is a large volcano that erupts frequently. It is over 10,000 ft (3300 metres) high and measures 25 miles (40 km) across the base. In the last twenty years alone there have been over forty eruptions, most of which have been from one of the

Lava reaching up to the first storey of the volcanological observatory on Mount Etna in 1971, shortly before the building was engulfed.

four summit craters, but a few have occurred at new sites down the slopes of the mountain. It is the latter, known as flank eruptions, that cause the most damage as they tend to be nearer the centres of population.

Summit eruptions at Etna can be very long-lived and persistent, and since 1955 there has been a great increase in the volume of lava erupted from the summit. From 1966 until 1971 there was almost continuous seepage of lava from the foot of the Northeast Crater. This accumulated into a field of lava extending about 2½ miles (4 km) down the northern slopes and was over 500 ft (150 metres) thick in places.

The 1971 eruption began on 5 April when, at 7.30 a.m., Antonio Nicoloso, one of the local guides from the town of Nicolosi, saw dark clouds of fume and ash rising from behind the volcano observatory on the south flank. He went to the scene at once and found that two new fissures had opened in the ground and that lava was pouring down the southern slopes. Small cones had already started to build up from the small explosions of molten lava. The flows caused concern at once, for they were heading straight for the observatory and the tourist installations of the south flank. They brushed past the observatory the following day and in four days were 1 mile (2 km) long.

On 8 April three Frenchmen decided to spend the night at the observatory, now surrounded on three sides by the accumulating lava. Heat was already conducting through the walls and the heavy iron doors were slowly beginning to deform. Every so often huge boulders brought down by the flow rolled against the outside walls, making the whole building shake. Needless to say, the Frenchmen were glad to leave the site of their disturbed night's sleep.

Amazingly, the observatory walls withstood the lava for two weeks while it climbed up to roof level, then the entire building suddenly disappeared one night without further trace. Meanwhile, the lava was causing concern lower down. The upper station of the cableway was slowly being overcome and the steel cable-car pylons twisted and buckled, slowly toppling over. Whenever the lava crossed a snow gully, the trapped snow turned to steam, causing pressure to build up. The resulting explosions, which occur without warning, are very dangerous, but on this occasion produced no casualties.

On 21 April an earthquake on the lower eastern slopes of the mountain brought down some houses in the towns of Sciara and Giarre. This was to be an important turning point in the course of the eruption. The following day a third crater opened higher up and slightly to the west of the others, adding a new stream of lava which joined the main flow lower down.

The main worry for the hundreds of people who make their living from the extensive tourist facilities on the south flank was the imminent destruction of the entire cableway. The cable-car ascent, which operates in both winter and summer, consisted of two separate stages, with a changeover station in the middle. The top cableway was already virtually destroyed and the lava was now perilously close to the intermediate station, threatening the lower cableway too. There was much discussion as to whether bulldozers should be used to divert the flow, but the problem was where to steer it. Anyone diverting a lava flow is legally responsible for any subsequent damage it may cause.

In the end, bulldozers were hardly necessary as the intermediate station was on a slight promontory, but the flow was deftly steered into a narrow valley to avoid two critical pylons on the lower cableway. However, even this neat solution posed problems as the tongue of lava began advancing rapidly downhill towards the Sapienza Hotel, which was full of guests. In the ensuing panic, preparations were made for evacuation at any moment.

However, changes within the volcano associated with the earthquake suddenly took the pressure off the south flank and moved the centre of the drama to a completely different part of the mountain. On 29 April the Central Crater at the top of the mountain began to emit thick clouds of ash and cinders, and new cracks began appearing in the ground to the east and southeast of the summit cone. A week later one of these began emitting gas under increasing pressure, then fragments of molten lava, and within a few hours a new cone was constructed, with lava pouring down the eastern slopes into the Valle del Bove, a huge, desolate valley nearly 3300 ft (1000 metres) deep and 3 miles (5 km) wide. From this time the flows on the south side began to decline, and stopped a few days later.

On 7 May a series of cracks up to 2 miles (3 km) long opened northeastwards from this new vent, heading towards the northern wall of the Valle del Bove. These emitted gas and lava flows at several points, but they were all short-lived. The cracks spread downhill a further mile (2 km) and on 11 and 12 May two much larger flows began to pour out from the end of this fissure system, over 3 miles (5 km) east of the summit.

It was immediately obvious that these flows presented much more of a threat. They travelled rapidly and on the evening of the 11th they had already cut off the Mareneve road 2 miles (3 km) from the fissure and were advancing towards the town of Fornazzo, destroying orchards, chestnut groves and vineyards.

Etna, in common with most other volcanoes, is not usually dangerous and no one was killed or even hurt in this eruption, but the damage caused to individuals and communities can still be devastating. It is a sickening sight to see lava slowly destroying a house or a lovingly tended vineyard. There is a particularly moving sequence of film showing a peasant woman just outside Fornazzo observing the lava slowly travelling towards her small house. In a curious, futile gesture she actually locks the old wooden door and stands to watch. Her face, beautifully etched and browned by seventy Sicilian summers of hard work on the land, is held proudly erect and yet charged with emotion. As the walls of her home tumble in clouds of dust and her vineyard succumbs over an agonizingly extended half hour, the tears slowly trickle down the furrows in her cheeks. Equally harrowing to watch is the panic ahead of the flow as villagers move out belongings and then begin unscrewing everything that might possibly be of value, such as doors, tap fittings and picture rails. Peasants cannot afford the high premiums to insure against such loss, so they have nothing to show for years of work; home and land disappear forever.

In the end, the lavas just clipped the edge of Fornazzo and comparatively few buildings were destroyed. For one month the lava continued to advance over agricultural land and some buildings, but the main damage had been done and the flows gradually slowed down and stopped. At the summit the southeast side of the cone had given way to form a collapse pit (see p. 46) from which ashy explosions occasionally issued, but all activity ceased by 12 June.

This was the twelfth flank eruption to occur on Etna this century and the sixth to cause destruction of buildings and agricultural land. But like many other volcanic areas, people will continue to be attracted there by the fertile soil volcanoes produce. Some of the 1971 lava has already been built on or covered with earth brought from elsewhere so that crops can be grown. At present the farmers are winning against the lava in the fight for land.

2
IN THE BEGINNING

THE FORMATION OF THE SOLAR SYSTEM

Volcanic activity is not a remote or minor danger; in fact, volcanoes past and present make up much of the Earth's surface. In order to understand how they work, how they were formed and how we can predict their activity to protect human lives and property, we have to dig deep into the Earth's history, back to the formation of the solar system itself.

Most meteorites are about 4.6 million years old and the oldest rocks on the Moon suggest that it was also formed then. Study of lead isotopes in the Earth's crust point to a similar date for the Earth, so it is very probable that the rest of the planets came into being at about the same time. The solar system in those days must have been a very different place from the stable, ordered arrangement we know today. A great whirlpool of dust, gas and chunks of rock swirled around the Sun in a nebulous disc. Gradually, most of this whirlpool condensed into solid lumps of rock, though precisely how this occurred is still a matter of some debate. Once these accumulations were large enough, their own gravitational force would have been sufficient to attract other solid particles to fall towards them. In this way the planets formed, gradually building up their size by accretion until they reached their present dimensions.

In the final stages of growth the planets in the solar system must have been a spectacular sight, with rocks up to the size of small planetoids crashing into them at terrific velocity. Each of these rocks would have formed an impact crater, and the larger and faster the impacting body, the larger the crater. The Moon, Mercury, Mars and many satellites of the outer planets still show the scars of this bombardment and are covered with impact craters. The largest of them, such as the Moon's Mare Imbrium, 600 miles (1000 km) in diameter, and Mercury's Caloris Basin, 800 miles (1300 km) across, were formed from the impact of planetoids so large that they very nearly split their targets and broke them into pieces. This was once thought to have happened to a small planet between Mars and Jupiter, as there is a wide gap between their orbits and hundreds of small asteroids, or minor planets, circle the sun between them.

Some of the planets also acquired their own systems of satellites orbiting around them, each like a mini solar system. To see how these came into being, we have to look at some of the consequences of the laws of motion and gravity. There is a delicate balance in operation between the force of gravity, which will tend to pull any two objects in space together, and the centrifugal force as two objects spin around each other, which will tend to pull them apart. A man who jumps off the Eiffel Tower will fall straight to the ground because he has no sideways velocity, but an astronaut who steps out of an orbiting spacecraft does not fall to Earth because he is travelling in a circle around the planet at a speed that keeps him balanced between centrifugal force which is pulling him away from the Earth as strongly as the gravitational force is pulling him towards it. The astronaut's speed has to be just right, however – too fast and he moves away from the Earth, too slow and the force of gravity dominates so he spirals back into it.

In the early history of the solar system most solid bodies approaching a planet would either have hit it or missed it altogether. However, some of those bodies travelling at the right speed and distance would have been captured by its gravitational pull and ended up circling it. All the planets acquired satellites in this way, except Venus and Mercury, and the larger planets attracted larger numbers of satellites. Jupiter and Saturn, for example, have thirty-five between them at present. The Earth's moon, however, may be a special case. It is about one quarter of the Earth's diameter, comparatively much larger than the satellites of any other planet, and bigger than Pluto, so the Earth–Moon system is often referred to as a double planet rather than a planet and satellite. The Moon could have formed at the same time as the Earth, or even have been created from the Earth following a large impact.

Thus the solar system gradually evolved as we know it today, with nine major planets orbiting the Sun and most of the planets having smaller satellites orbiting them. The largest planets and satellites have sufficient gravitational pull to retain some of the gas from the early stages of planetary formation. In the case of Jupiter and Saturn, and to some extent Uranus and Neptune also, these atmospheres are very thick and constitute a major part of the planet. At the other end

OVERLEAF: (top) The solar system 4600 million years ago: a great whirlpool of dust, gas and rocks. (bottom) A few million years later, the planets have started to form by accretion.

of the scale, Mars has little gravitational pull so it has retained a very thin atmosphere and also some water, while Mercury is too small and too close to the Sun to have any pull, so it has no atmosphere. (The molecules of gas would have been travelling at speeds which exceeded the escape velocity of the planet.)

Most of the Earth's atmosphere and water has come from volcanic outgassing of the interior, a process that is still going on today. The difference that an atmosphere and surface water can make to a planet is illustrated by the Earth and the Moon. They are at an identical mean distance from the Sun, but the Moon is too small to retain an atmosphere. It has never had any surface water, so erosion is extremely slow, leaving lavas and impact craters 4000 million years old clearly visible. The Earth's surface, however, is continuously being eroded by water, ice, wind and chemical action, the combined power of which wears away rocks to powder and forms new rocks by deposition. Major landforms can be eroded flat or buried by newer rocks in less than a million years.

The presence of water and an atmosphere have also meant one other important difference from the Moon. The Earth, apparently alone among the planets of the solar system, has been able to develop life. Very primitive forms of life have now been found in some of the oldest rocks on Earth, 3500 million years old, and it is probable that lightning, water and volcanic gases were all involved in creating the first building blocks of life. However, the evolution into even slighty more complex forms took another 2000 million years or so, and it was not until 3000 million years later that the first plants appeared on the land.

THE EVOLUTION OF THE EARTH

The primitive solar nebula of dust and gas may originally have been very hot, particularly at the centre where the Sun was formed. Since temperature determines whether a given element is a solid or a gas, distance from the heat source of the Sun will also have played an important part in determining the original composition of the accreting planet. The Earth is one of the nearer planets to the Sun, so only those elements and compounds with high enough melting-points to be solid could start to accrete, and this is true of Mercury, Venus and Mars also. The larger outer planets such as Jupiter, however, which were formed further from the Sun in colder regions, were able to accrete lighter elements with lower melting-points, particularly compounds of hydrogen, nitrogen, carbon and oxygen, and they still retain a much higher percentage of these elements today.

Thus, the Earth began as an accumulation of mostly higher melting-point elements, such as silica, magnesium and iron, accreted as a homogeneous mass, with elements equally distributed throughout the planet. Some scientists believe that in the early stages of planetary formation, the largest masses of solid rock to collect together under the force of gravity, which eventually formed the planets, may have been relatively cold at the time they were building up by accretion, particularly in the outer regions away from the Sun. However, as they got bigger, forces came into play that caused their interiors to heat up.

In the first place, the very process of accretion, with the continuous bombardment of the surface by chunks of rock up to several miles wide, causes heat by loss of kinetic energy, which slowly accumulates inside the Earth. In the second place, the heat given off by the steady decay of radioactive elements within the planet will steadily accumulate throughout the entire planet. Also, the simple process of increasing pressure within the planet as it gets bigger will produce heat by compression, the temperature increasing towards the centre of the planet. Once the planetary interior is heated up sufficiently to melt or partially melt a large percentage of the planet, differentiation or segregation of the various chemical elements into different depths within the planet can occur on a large scale.

Within the Earth the lighter elements tended to float to the surface, and a layered structure developed with heavier elements, particularly iron, sinking to the centre of the planet to form a core. Above this would have been a silicate mantle. This actual process of core formation also generates heat, for like any falling object, the heavy elements acquire kinetic energy which is given off as heat when they come to rest at the centre of the Earth.

Strangely enough, the formation of the core can be dated, for the magnetic field of the Earth, which is generated within the core could not have existed beforehand. The oldest rocks on Earth, 3700 million years old, have *remanent magnetization*, so the core must already have been in place by then. More importantly, the study of lead isotopes within the Earth's crust give a date for their formation of 4550 million years, slightly younger than meteorites, which have been put at 4600 million years old. It has been suggested that 4550 million years, the age when the Earth's 'atomic

Early in the history of the solar system, when meteorite impacts were still commonplace, the Moon was much closer to the Earth.

clocks' were set, is not the date when the Earth was formed, but rather the date of core formation, when most of the lead sank to the centre.

Consequently, the Earth was at its hottest soon after its formation, when the outer 250 miles (400 km) was probably molten. Since then, heat production has steadily declined and continued cooling will eventually lead to 'geological death', when the Earth will become rigid throughout and earth movements and volcanic activity will cease. Shortly after the Earth's formation, however, there must have been a considerable amount of 'outgassing' at the surface – the principal constituent and driving force of volcanic activity – but details of this earliest volcanic activity cannot be known, though it was probably more chaotic and on a far greater scale than any volcanic activity witnessed today. At the same time, the Earth continued to be bombarded with asteroid-sized bodies for another 500 million years, after which bombardment declined, but even now has not quite finished.

The Earth's atmosphere has also changed greatly throughout its history. The early atmosphere was probably composed mainly of carbon dioxide, with smaller amounts of nitrogen, water vapour and traces of other elements. This is close to the composition of the atmospheres of Mars and Venus, our two closest planetary neighbours. As the water condensed to form the oceans, much of the carbon dioxide was dissolved in them. Tiny amounts of water vapour in the early atmosphere of the Earth would have been broken down into its constituent parts, hydrogen and oxygen, by ultraviolet light from the Sun. Hydrogen is the lightest element and would have been lost into space, but the oxygen would have been retained.

The big change came when plants appeared. They lived by taking in carbon dioxide from the atmosphere and expelling oxygen under the action of sunlight, a process known as *photosynthesis.* This steadily cut down the amount of carbon dioxide in the atmosphere to its present level of about 0.03 per cent, while increasing the oxygen from about 0.001 to 21 per cent, its present value. This increase in oxygen became marked about 2200 million years ago, when Old Red Sandstones first appear in the geological record. Areas of light continental crust were already well established by this time, for they had begun to appear about 3700 million years ago.

The Earth gradually evolved its present internal structure, with a solid inner core of an iron-nickel alloy stretching from the centre of the Earth, nearly

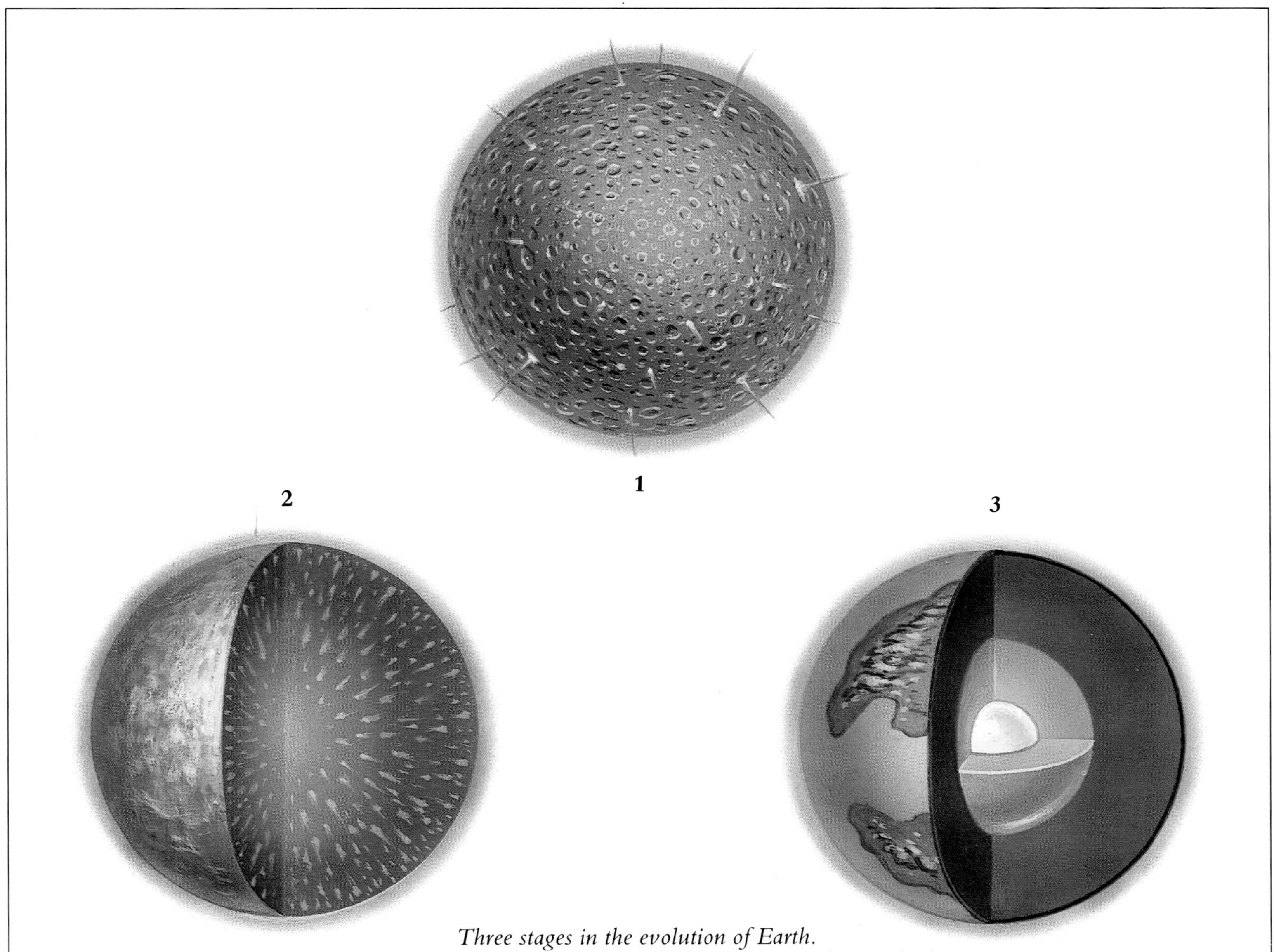

Three stages in the evolution of Earth.
1 *Millions of solid rocks up to several kilometres across crash into the Earth, forming craters.*
2 *Internal and impact heating causes differentiation. Metals and heavy materials sink, lighter materials rise to form a crust.*
3 *Over 3 billion years ago water in the atmosphere has condensed to form seas and continents have formed, ravaged by volcanic activity. Crustal plates have not yet appeared.*

4000 miles (6400 km) beneath our feet, to a depth of just over 3000 miles (5100 km), where the transition to the liquid outer core of iron with some sulphur occurs. Above this, at a depth of nearly 1800 miles (2900 km), begins the mantle, composed of silicate rocks, which comprises two-thirds of the Earth's mass. On the basis of differences in density, this can be divided into the lower mantle, the upper mantle and a transition zone between them. The mantle is solid on a short time-scale, but the slow creep of its upper part, which includes partially molten material, is responsible for one of the most important processes in shaping the Earth as we know it today: continental drift.

The mantle is covered by the Earth's crust, the thinnest layer of all, varying in thickness from as little as 3 miles (5 km) in some parts of the oceans to depths of 55 miles (90 km) beneath the thickest parts of the continents. The crust can be divided into two different types: oceanic crust which is 3–6 miles (5–10 km) thick, and continental crust which varies from 12–55 miles (20–90 km) thick. The continental crust, where silica and aluminium compounds predominate, is lighter than the oceanic crust, in which silica and magnesium compounds are more important, and 'floats' upon it.

3
VOLCANOES AND PLATE TECTONICS

PLATE TECTONICS AND CONTINENTAL DRIFT

Within the mantle of the Earth the temperature increases with increasing depth and this produces a fundamental instability. The situation is similar to heating a saucepan of soup on a stove. The heat from below warms the soup at the bottom of the saucepan, so it expands, becoming lighter than the soup above it. It therefore rises to replace the cold soup at the top, which moves aside and sinks down to the bottom of the saucepan at the edges. This cold soup is then heated until hotter than the soup above it, so it also rises up the centre to displace the surface liquid. The constant rising of hot liquid in the middle and descending of cooling liquid at the edges is known as *convection* and becomes very fast and obvious when the soup boils.

A similar situation occurs within the Earth's mantle and is known as *mantle convection*. In certain places the lower and hotter parts of the mantle are rising through the mantle above, which is displaced sideways for great distances by the new material arriving from below. This displaced colder material then sinks down again into the mantle at another site which may be thousands of miles away. The rising parts of the mantle tend to reach the surface at long, linear cracks that run for great distances across the surface of the Earth. These are variously known as *spreading axes*, *constructive plate margins*, or *divergent boundaries*. The surface rises to form a ridge on either side of these cracks which is called a *mid-ocean ridge* as it tends to occur in the middle of the vast stretches of oceanic crust beneath the sea. The continental crust, floating on the denser oceanic crust, is moved apart by the sideways forces of convection and thus, over millions of years, the continents slowly drift about across the surface of the Earth in response to the patterns of convection within the mantle.

The other end of the convection cell, where the surface crust sinks down again into the mantle, is known as a *subduction zone*. Like the mid-ocean ridges, these areas are long, linear features and often occur at the edges of continents, where the oceanic crust, now cooler and heavier than the mantle rocks and much heavier than the continental crust, sinks beneath it back into the mantle. As the heavy crust sinks, it drags down the surface with it, so deep trenches in the sea floor are usually found above a subduction zone. The deepest sea on Earth, 7 miles (10.9 km) below sea level, is at the bottom of the ocean trench south of the Mariana Islands in the western Pacific.

The surface of the Earth may therefore be thought of as a series of crustal plates floating on the mantle beneath. At one end of the plate – the constructive margin – material is rising from the mantle to form new crust, causing the rest of the plate to move laterally away from this margin at speeds which are presently measured at more than 4 in (10 cm) per year in some cases. At the other end of the plate, known as a *destructive margin*, or *convergent boundary*, the plate is being sucked down into the mantle again. There are also *conservative margins* at the sides where the plate is moving sideways against neighbouring plates, but no new crust is being created or old crust destroyed. Returning to the heated soup analogy, convergent boundaries can be created if liquid is heated in a wide pan over two gas rings; a 'subduction zone' is created between the two heat sources down which the surface crust of dried soup disappears.

There are currently seven large plates on the surface of the Earth: the Eurasian, the North American, the South American, the Antarctic, the African, the Indian and the Pacific. All except the Pacific plate have large portions of continental crust floating on them. There are also smaller plates: the Arabian, the Caribbean, the Cocos, the Nazca and the Philippine, of which only the first two have sizeable pieces of continental crust. There are also probably other smaller 'platelets' in regions where the tectonic situation is complex.

The distribution of volcanoes and earthquakes over the surface of the Earth is intimately linked to the position and movements of these plates. The mid-ocean ridges are the sites of considerable outpourings of lava, but most of these eruptions are unknown and unobserved because they occur beneath the sea. The destructive margins are the sites of a different type of volcanism, not always so frequent, but often more violent and dangerous than at constructive plate margins. Both margins also have earthquakes associated with the constant movement occurring there, but they tend to be larger and much more frequent at destruc-

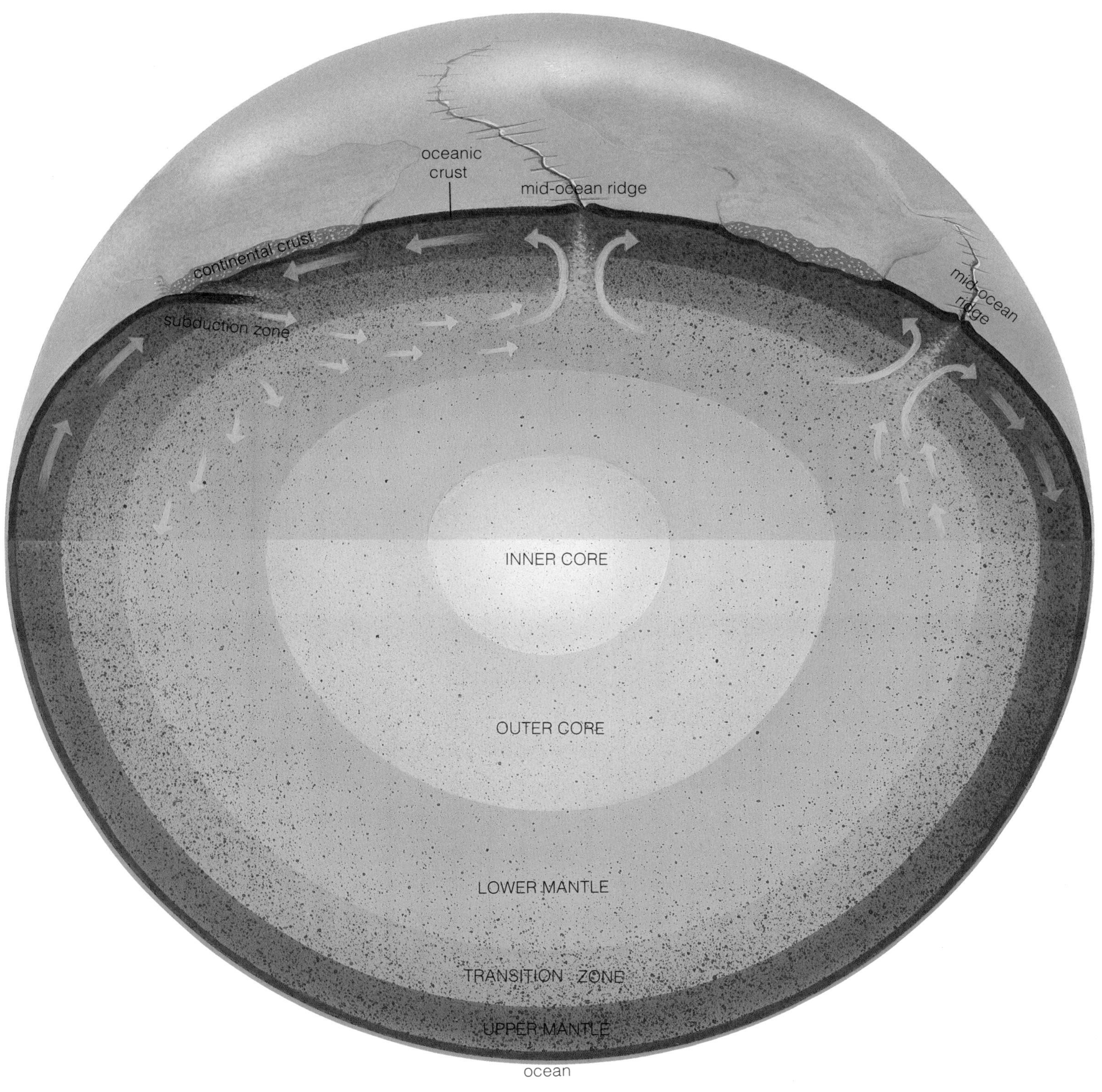

The present structure of the Earth, with arrows showing convective movements in the mantle. Rising currents occur at mid-ocean ridges, and descending currents at subduction zones, where crust is dragged down into the mantle.

Map of the world's tectonic plates, and active or recently active volcanoes. Arrows show the direction of movement of the different plates.

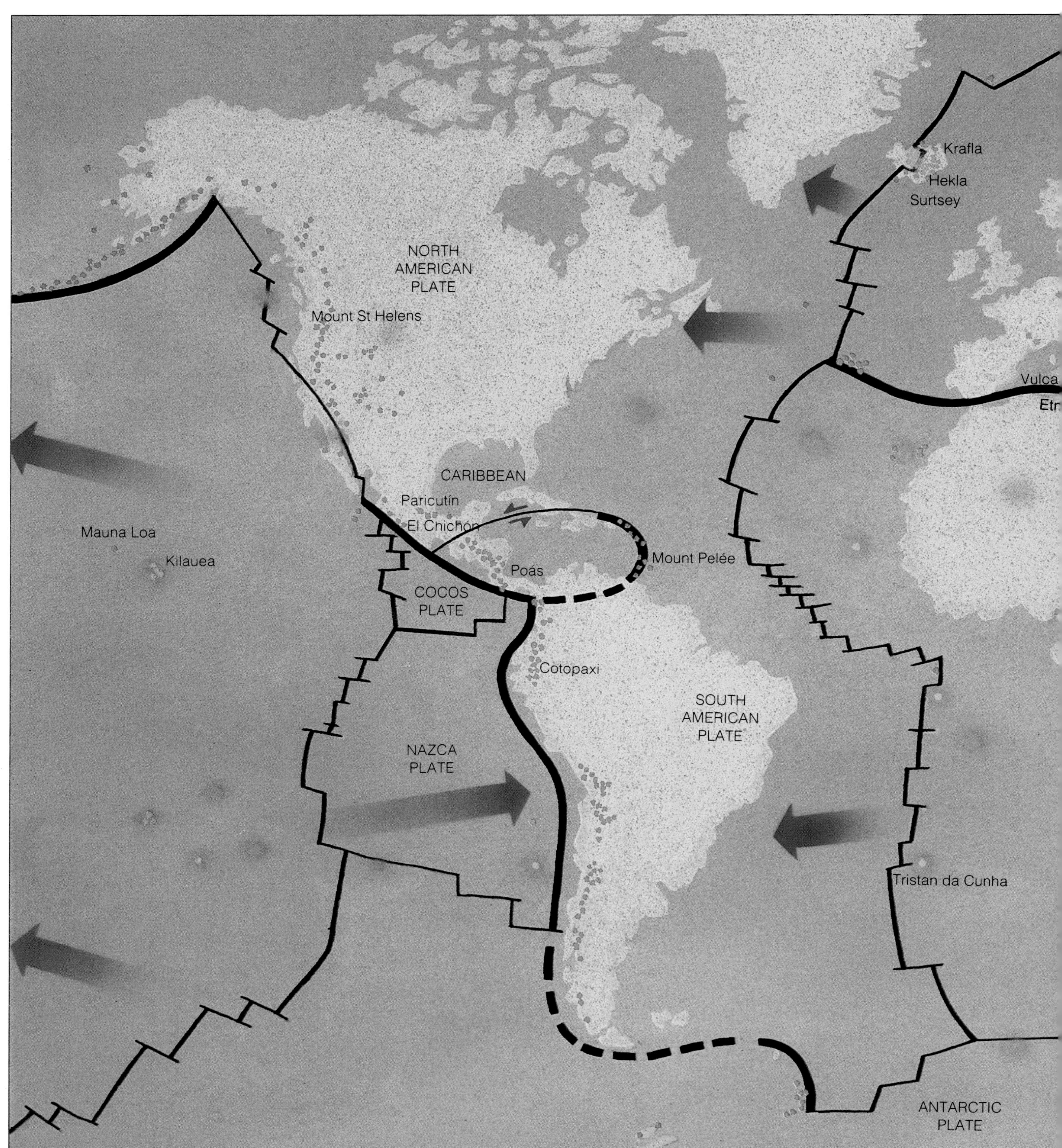

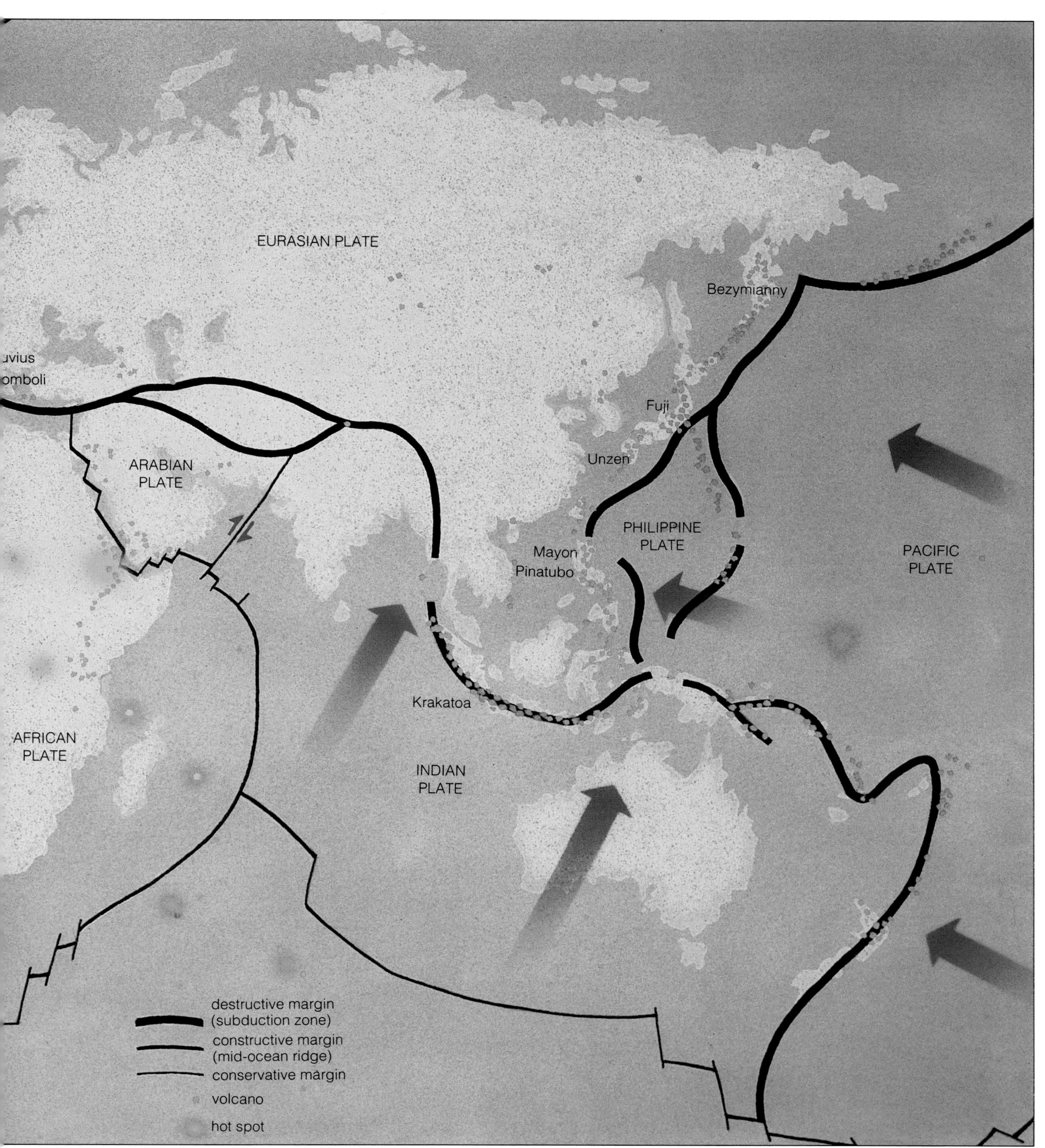
EURASIAN PLATE
Bezymianny
uvius
omboli
Fuji
Unzen
ARABIAN PLATE
PHILIPPINE PLATE
Mayon
Pinatubo
PACIFIC PLATE
Krakatoa
AFRICAN PLATE
INDIAN PLATE
destructive margin (subduction zone)
constructive margin (mid-ocean ridge)
conservative margin
volcano
hot spot

Volcanoes worldwide: (TOP TO BOTTOM) Ash ring in Ethiopia; Krakatoa, Indonesia; Didicas volcano, Philippines.

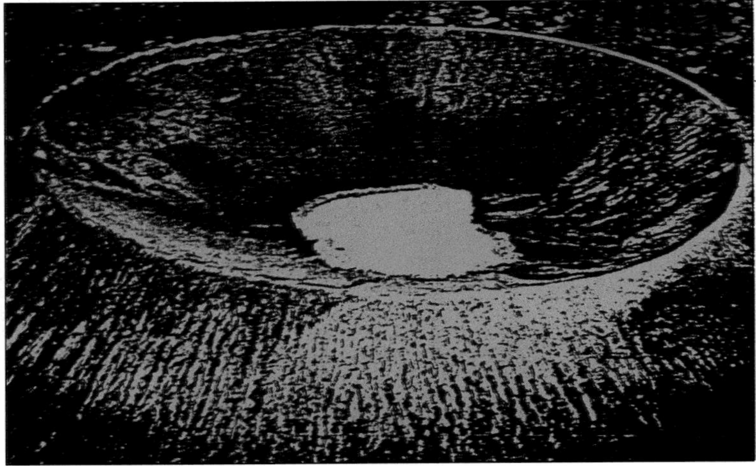

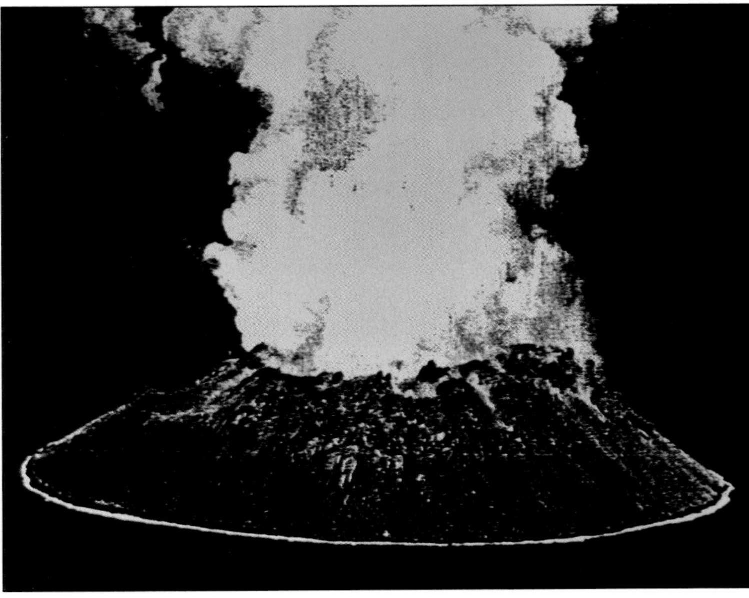

tive margins where the plate is forcing its way down into the mantle.

In some areas plate motions have brought two masses of continental crust together. When this happens, virtually no subduction occurs because the continents are of the same density, both floating on the denser oceanic crust. Instead, a zone of compression is formed and mountains are thrown up as the two continents are squeezed together. This has happened where the Indian plate has come against the Eurasian plate in the last few million years. The Indian plate was travelling fast and its collison with Eurasia threw up the Himalayan Mountains, now the highest on Earth.

The present system of plate motion and continental drift can be traced back to a mere 200 million years ago, geological evidence suggesting that all the present continents were grouped together as a single 'super-continent'. However, geological evidence from present-day continents such as Africa show signs of much earlier plate movements, so it is probable that similar processes have operated before. In the first 1000 million years of the Earth's history, however, it is likely that lighter continental material had not yet separated from the mantle, so no continents existed on the first mobile plates of those times.

VOLCANOES WORLDWIDE

There are currently around 500 known active volcanoes on the Earth's surface, but many more unknown volcanoes, recently active ones, or volcanic areas that could become active at any time. Volcanoes can be immensely destructive as well as having economic value, so their careful study and continuous monitoring is very important to those countries in which they occur. Unfortunately, the poverty of some nations in highly active volcanic areas is such that only limited monitoring is possible.

By far the greater number of volcanoes occur near constructive or destructive plate margins. Those at constructive plate margins are the least known, as most of them lie on mid-ocean ridges beneath the sea. However, they can be studied in Iceland, for example, where the Mid-Atlantic Ridge rises above sea level, also in the Azores, at Tristan da Cunha in the South Atlantic and Jan Mayen in the far North Atlantic. The Galapagos Islands in the Pacific are also on a small mid-ocean ridge between the Cocos and the Nazca plates in the eastern Pacific Ocean. Other active volcanoes, such as Piton de la Fournaise on Réunion Island in the Indian

FROM TOP: Sunset Crater, Arizona; Cinder core beneath Mauna Kea, Hawaii; Mayon volcano, Philippines; Fire fountaining at Kilauea volcano, Hawaii.

Ocean, are close to mid-ocean ridges.

Most of the world's subaerial (as opposed to submarine) volcanoes are found close to destructive plate margins. These include the violent volcanoes of Indonesia, such as Krakatoa, Kelut and Tambora, and those of New Guinea and the New Hebrides. All these volcanoes are on the northern margin of the Indian plate, where it is being subducted beneath the Eurasian and Pacific plates. The eastnortheast motion of the large Pacific plate gives rise to more volcanic activity than any other, with subduction zones along the Aleutian Islands and Alaska, which include the volcanoes Katmai and Novarupta, and also the Kurile Islands and Kamchatka, where Bezymianny volcano lies. This subduction zone divides at Japan, which has many active volcanoes such as Mount Fuji and Sakurajima, and continues through the Bonin and the Mariana Islands further south. A separate Pacific subduction zone runs from the Samoa Islands down through Tonga to New Zealand, which has many active volcanoes, including Ruapehue and White Island, as well as some violent prehistoric volcanoes.

Two small subduction zones are associated with the relatively small westward motion of the North and South American plates; these have given rise to the Caribbean volcanoes, such as Mount Pelée and La Soufrière, and the South Sandwich Islands. The rapid movement of the smaller Nazca plate in the East Pacific has produced the Andes volcanoes in South America, with the tragically destructive Nevado del Ruiz in the north and large volcanoes such as Chimborazo, Cotopaxi, El Misti and Villarrica further south. The even smaller Cocos plate, which is moving northeast, is responsible for the volcanoes of Central America, which include Paricutín, Popocatepetl, Poás and the recently destructive El Chichón. The Philippine Islands on the other side of the Pacific Ocean are also the site of a large subduction zone bordering a small plate. Mount Unzen in Japan and Mount Pinatubo in the Philippines both lie on this plate and were the scene of dramatic eruptions in June 1991.

Other well-known volcanoes at plate boundaries occur in complex areas or in tectonic situations which are, as yet, poorly understood. Lassen Peak and Mount St Helens, the recently active volcanoes of North America, may be close to a small subduction zone, and the famous volcanoes of the Mediterranean – Etna, Vesuvius, Stromboli, Vulcano and Santorini – all lie between the colliding continents of Africa and Eurasia, and may be associated with small subduction zones.

RIGHT: Large earthquakes can cause major damage to roads which are crossed by faults and fissures. Buildings have to be specially constructed to withstand large shocks in earthquake-prone regions.

Some volcanic areas are particularly interesting in that they lie in the middle of large plates. The Hawaiian Islands, which include Kilauea and Mauna Loa, probably the two best-studied volcanoes in the world, and the volcanoes of the East African Rift, such as the huge Kilimanjaro, fall into this category. Hawaii appears to lie on a 'hot spot' or mantle plume, where a small area of rising mantle has created local volcanism, while the East African Rift may be an incipient spreading axis, with the continent of Africa just beginning to split apart.

EARTHQUAKES

Most earthquakes occur where the 'creeping' of one part of the Earth relative to another – particularly the slow movement of one plate relative to another –

Mercalli Scale	*Approx. equivalent on Richter scale at depth of 6 miles (10 km)*
1. Not felt, except under ideal conditions.	—
2. Felt by a few at rest. Delicately suspended objects swing.	2.5
3. Felt noticeably indoors. Standing cars may rock.	—
4. Felt generally indoors. People awakened, windows rattled.	3.5
5. Felt generally. Some falling plaster; dishes, windows broken.	—
6. Felt by all. Chimneys damaged, furniture moved, difficult to walk.	—
7. People run outdoors. Felt in moving cars. Moderate damage.	5.5
8. General alarm. Damage to weak structures; monuments and walls fall.	6.0
9. Total destruction of weak structures; ground fissured.	7.0
10. Panic. Strongest buildings survive, ground badly cracked, rails bent.	—
11. Few buildings survive. Broad fissures, underground pipes broken	8.0
12. Total destruction. Ground waves seen, uncontrollable panic.	8.5

Large earthquakes that occur close to or beneath the sea can create sea waves called tsunamis. Although they may be only a few feet high out to sea, they increase in height as they near the shore and do immense damage as they reach land.

builds up strain in the ground. This strain will be abruptly released when rock failure occurs and the ground jumps suddenly, causing an earthquake. This can happen at any depth within the mantle, but the most destructive earthquakes occur relatively near the surface, usually along well-defined geological faults. The ground may shift up to 16 ft (5 metres) in the largest earthquakes, or less than half an inch (1 cm) in small ones.

The strength of an earthquake is usually measured on one of two scales: the Mercalli scale of intensity and the Richter scale of magnitude. The Mercalli scale is not a precise one and is used only to indicate the destructive intensity of an earthquake at a particular point on the Earth's surface. Consequently, the same earthquake will give different values on the Mercalli scale according to how far the observer is from the *epicentre*, the point on the Earth's surface that lies directly above the earthquake. Nevertheless, the Mercalli scale is simple and conveys an immediate idea of the power of the shock at a given place.

The Richter scale is intended to measure absolutely the energy released during the earthquake. It is a logarithmic scale, so an earthquake of magnitude 6 is ten times more powerful than one of magnitude 5, an earthquake of magnitude 7 is ten times more powerful than magnitude 6, and so on.

The massive Lisbon earthquake of 1755 probably measured about 8.9 on the Richter scale. More recently, a quake measuring 8.6 hit the town of Anchorage in Alaska on Good Friday, 1964. Cars disappeared down huge cracks that fissured the streets and widespread destruction of buildings occurred. The town was 100 miles (160 km) from the epicentre, but the ground rose and fell over a distance of hundreds of miles.

MID-OCEAN RIDGES

The most prominent of the mid-ocean ridges are the Mid-Atlantic Ridge and the East Pacific Rise. The former was the first to be discovered and is also the best known as large areas of it are exposed above the sea in Iceland. The ridge is a broad, shallow-sloping rise over 1000 miles (1600 km) wide and 10,000 miles

(16,000 km) long, with the top about 1–2 miles (2–3 km) higher than the sea floor either side. The crest is marked by a rift valley where volcanic eruptions and earthquakes occur. This crest lies directly over the rising parts of the large convection currents within the Earth's mantle and is important as the site where new oceanic crust is created.

The earth's magnetic field suffers polarity reversals (i.e. the magnetic north switches to the Earth's south pole and vice versa) after irregular intervals of tens of thousands to millions of years, and solidifying lava from an erupting volcano will preserve part of the Earth's magnetic field at the time of its cooling as remanent magnetization. The recent lavas erupted at the centre of the Mid-Atlantic Ridge have a magnetization with the north magnetic pole pointing north, since they were erupted under the Earth's present-day magnetic field direction. However, a few miles from the centre, the polarity of the rocks suddenly reverses, and then still further from the centre reverses back to present-day polarity. This pattern is repeated from the centre of the ridge across the ocean floor to the continental edges and is symmetrical on either side of the ridge.

These reversals of magnetic polarity are also found in the remanent magnetization of basalt lavas that have been erupted on the land over the same time interval. Since the dates of these basalts can be measured by isotopic dating methods, the dates of the Earth's magnetic reversals are now well known. Using this data, the dates of lavas erupted from the ocean floor during magnetic reversals can also be determined. Assuming they were erupted at the ridge axis, their present distance from this is a measure of how far the ocean floor has spread since the date of eruption.

These calculations show that the floor of the Atlantic Ocean is spreading at a rate of about 1 in (2 cm) per year, but parts of the Pacific Ocean are moving at more

Mid-ocean ridges are the sites of upwelling in the mantle. This causes basaltic volcanism and creates new oceanic crust, which spreads sideways. Mid-ocean ridges tend to be in short sections separated by transform faults. Occasionally, 'hot spots' manage to penetrate the oceanic crust as it moves over them, creating isolated volcanoes in the ocean.

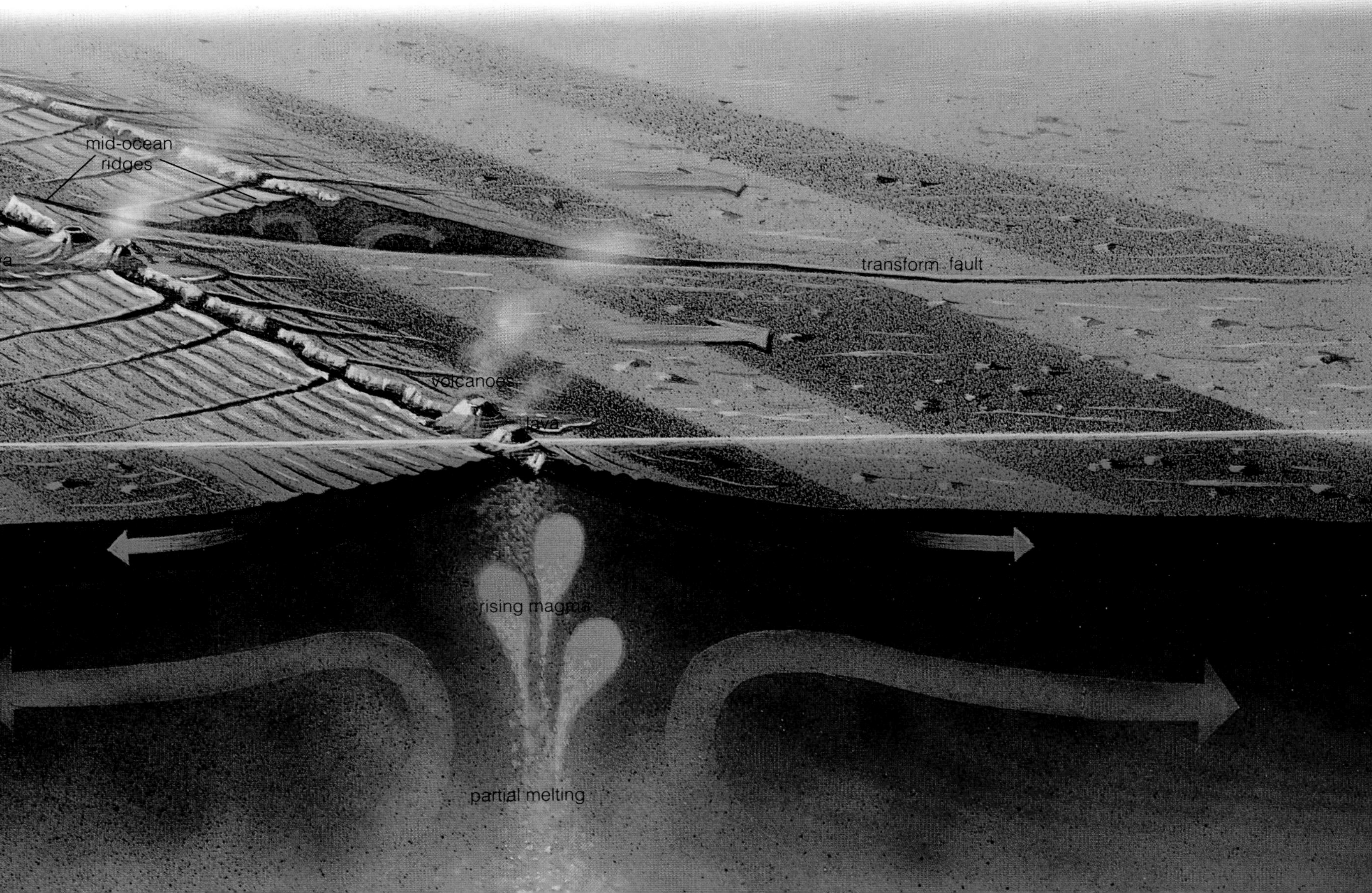

than 4 in (10 cm) a year. The actual details of what happens at the axis of the spreading ridge itself can be seen in Iceland. Fissure eruptions are common, not surprisingly as the continuous lateral movement causes tensional strain and opens deep faults and fissures up which lavas are erupted. This tensional faulting near the ridge axis causes long sections to be downfaulted to form rift valleys (known as *graben* when they occur on a small scale).

Beneath the ridge is the rising convection current in the mantle. Hotter parts of the mantle rise and the decrease in pressure allows them to melt partially, i.e. those elements and compounds in the mantle which have lower melting-points do so. These float up to form pockets of magma in the crust beneath the ridge axis. *Magma* is a general name for molten lava before it has erupted, but the two are chemically different as magma contains dissolved gases and sublimates which are lost into the atmosphere on eruption. As the ocean floor moves apart because of convection, magma rises up the resulting cracks and either erupts or is injected into the crust, where it in turn becomes new crust upon cooling

Although all mid-ocean ridges are characterized by earthquakes, they tend to be less frequent and less powerful than at other plate boundaries. It requires far less energy to split the land apart by tension than to force the crust to fold and buckle by compression, and lavas rise up the cracks passively, often in high-volume eruptions which can be devastating. The Laki Fissure, which opened in Iceland in 1783, continued to erupt very fluid lavas at a high rate for a period of six months. The total volume of lavas during this time was something like 3 cubic miles (11 cubic km), the largest known volume of all historic eruptions. Similar eruptions must also be taking place at mid-ocean ridges with comparative frequency, but remain unknown because of their location deep beneath the sea.

SUBDUCTION ZONES AND ISLAND ARCS

Some of the world's most violent volcanoes are found at the destructive plate margins, where the oceanic crust is dragged back down into the Earth to be absorbed into the mantle again. This descending part of the convective system is sometimes found against the edge of exposed continental crust, where it may buckle the crust to form fold mountains, as well as volcanoes. This may be seen in South America, where the Nazca plate descends beneath the Andes. In other places the subduction zone is beneath the sea and the associated volcanism breaks the surface as an *island arc*, such as the Aleutians or the Kurile Islands.

The mantle's convective system is complex, some convection taking place at a comparatively shallow depth. This near-surface convection depends upon the *low velocity zone*, so called because seismic waves travel through it more slowly. It is actually a layer near the top of the mantle at a depth of 40–150 miles (70–250 km), where the temperature is high enough and the pressure low enough for a tiny percentage of melting to occur.

The low velocity zone acts as a lubricating layer to the convective system, with the crust and upper mantle above it moving laterally and comparatively fast away from the mid-ocean ridges downhill towards the subduction zones. Beneath it a much greater thickness of mantle is creeping slowly in the opposite direction to rise up to the surface at the mid-ocean ridges. This part of the mantle is white-hot but solid, yet like the ice in a glacier it slowly deforms over the years and is capable of flowing on a very long time-scale. It is also possible that separate, deeper convection cells occur within the mantle.

Some observations suggest that the simple idea of a hot soup convection system (see p. 26) is not exactly appropriate to the convection in the Earth's mantle. The mid-ocean ridges, for example, although they extend for thousands of miles, are cut crossways by numerous *transform faults* that divide them into comparatively short sections, so the spreading along these faults is actually going in opposite directions between adjacent spreading axes. Since the ridge axes are a surface expression of convection in the mantle beneath, the convection cells would have to be extremely narrow – often less than 60 miles (100 km) – in relation to their length of thousands of miles. This therefore puts in doubt the idea that mantle convection is driven mainly by heating from below.

A more likely explanation comes from considerations of the situation at subduction zones. The slab of crust descending beneath the continent is colder and thus denser than its surroundings. It therefore sinks under its own weight, just as a stone will sink through water. Since it is attached to the rest of the oceanic crust, it will pull this crust with it; such 'slab-pull' is considered to be the dominant force driving convection in the mantle. It seems, therefore, that the hot parts in the mantle beneath mid-ocean ridges are *not* the driving forces of plate motion, so the analogy of

Subduction zones are the sites of downward movements, where oceanic crust is dragged down and reincorporated into the mantle. Volcanic mountain chains are formed where it descends below continental crust (left) or island arc volcanoes are formed where it descends below oceanic crust (right).

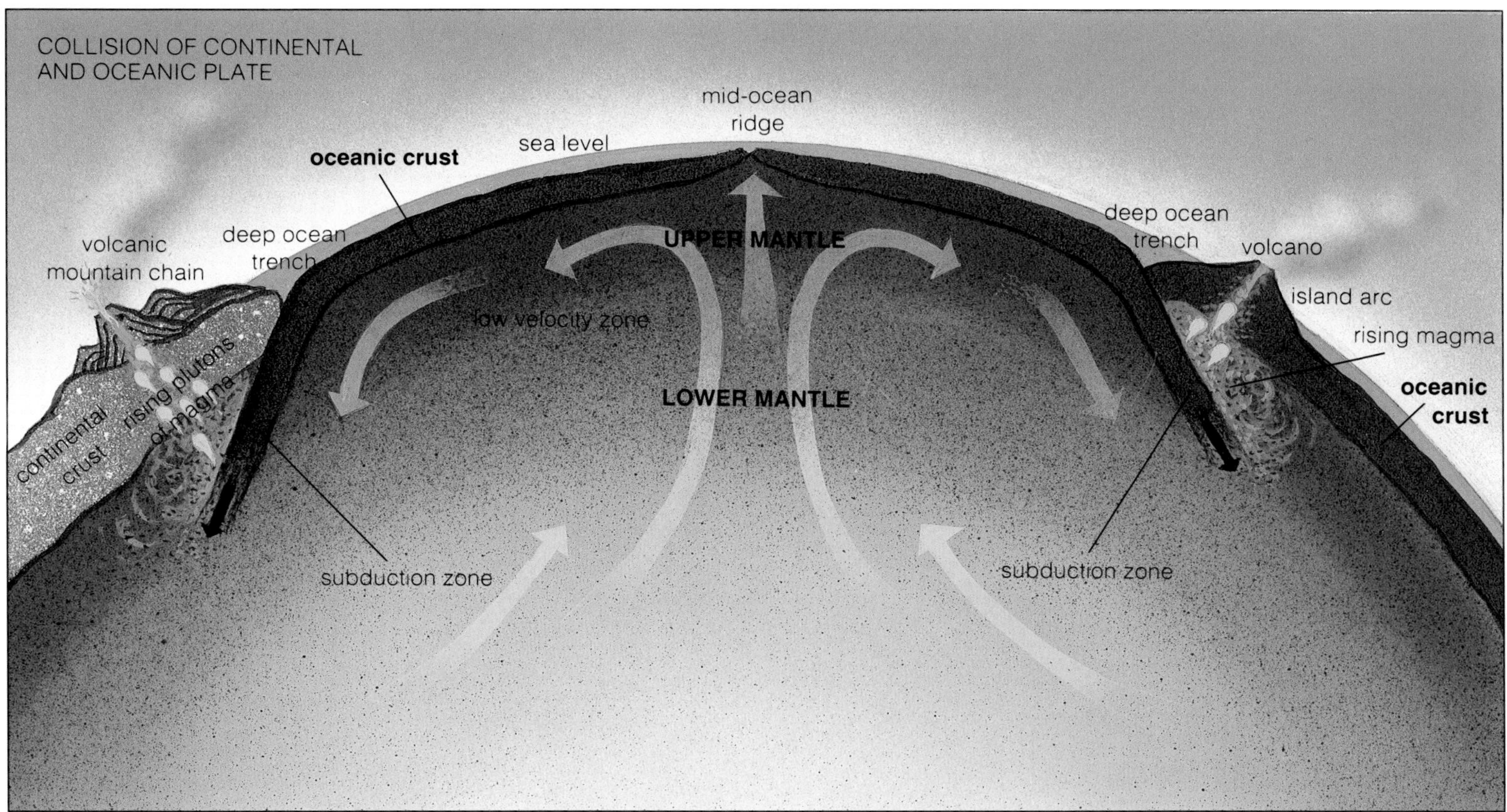

heated soup, though useful, should not be taken too far. Although the rise of the hot mantle plays some part, the sinking of the cold crust is probably the major force governing the drifting of the continents.

However, if the descending slab of crust is colder than its surroundings, why does the mantle melt here to form magma and volcanoes? In the first place, the friction of the descending slab against the continental crust and the mantle produces some heating at its edge, but more important is the effect of water. This will have combined with rocks on the ocean floor, which has the effect of lowering melting temperatures by up to several hundred degrees, so that when the cold slab descends and starts heating up, it will melt at temperatures much lower than the surrounding rocks. It may also release water into the surrounding rocks, allowing them to melt also. A third effect which sometimes occurs is the selective erosion of radioactive elements, which may be concentrated in part of the descending crust where the radioactive decay causes local heating.

These effects mean that pockets of magma are formed at depths of 30 miles (50 km) or more at the top of the subduction zone, beneath the edge of the continent. As they are hotter and less heavy than the surrounding rocks, they slowly rise through them, collecting into *plutons*, which are balloons of molten magma several miles across. The continuous accumulation or coalescence of several plutons over the ages may produce a *batholith* – a vast submerged mass of cooling magma which can be up to 1250 miles (2000 km) long.

The magmas which reach the surface at a subduction zone are far more varied in composition than at mid-ocean ridges. They may be basalts similar to those at ocean ridges, they may have evolved, or they may have melted various types of continental rock to form lavas with a higher silica content, such as andesites, rhyolites or any combination in between. Rhyolite lavas have the highest silica content and are said to be more *acidic* in composition. Acidic magmas give rise to a different type of volcanism which can be much more violent. Both Krakatoa and Mount Pelée, which have been described earlier, are mainly acidic volcanoes above subduction zones.

The descending oceanic crust also gives rise to many earthquakes as it is subducted into the mantle. Near the ocean deeps where the crust starts its descent into the mantle these earthquakes are fairly shallow, but further into the continent they become deeper and deeper, and the actual position of the descending slab can be inferred from their depth. These earthquakes cease when the slab reaches a depth of about 450 miles

The East African Rift Valley is a huge, fault-bounded, down-dropped trough.

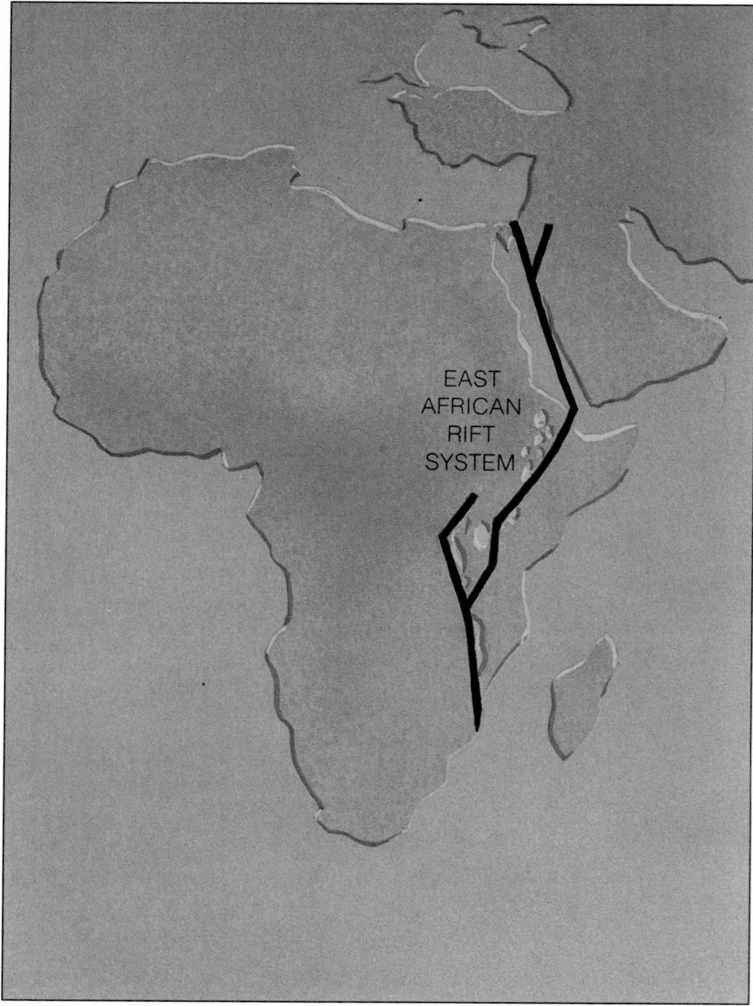

The Rift Valley appears to be splitting Africa in two. Further north it connects with the Red Sea, an incipient mid-ocean ridge system which has already split Arabia apart from Africa.

(700 km), where it has presumably ceased to be brittle enough for earthquakes to occur. However, the slab is still detectable below this level by the velocities of unrelated earthquake waves that pass through it, so it has clearly not completely merged with the mantle, even at this substantial depth and distance from the point of descent.

Earthquakes at subduction zones can be particularly destructive and the 1964 earthquake in Anchorage, Alaska, described earlier, was in this category, associated with the subduction zone beneath Alaska and the Aleutian Islands.

MID-PLATE VOLCANOES

Although most volcanic activity occurs at the edges of the rigid plates that make up the Earth's surface, some eruptions persistently occur in the centre of these plates, far from any mid-ocean ridges or subduction zones. They may either be in the middle of continents, such as Kilimanjaro and the other volcanoes of the East African Rift, or in oceans, such as the volcanoes on the Hawaiian Islands in the middle of the Pacific Ocean.

The East African Rift system is a prominent, straight-sided valley, or series of valleys, that runs north for thousands of miles from Tanzania to Ethiopia, where it joins the Red Sea (part of the same rift system). The valleys are bounded on both sides by prominent, straight faults, with the valley floors dropped down between them by up to ½ mile (1 km). Scattered along the length of the rift are a large number of active or recently active volcanoes. Some of them, such as Kilimanjaro, Mount Elgon and Mount Kenya, are large, central volcanoes that are or have been active over a long period. They erupt basaltic lavas, but of a distinct type with high sodium and potassium contents, known as alkali basalts.

The Red Sea is also remarkable, being so narrow that it seems to be a simple extension of the East African Rift flooded by the sea. Its composition, however, suggests that it is in fact an ocean floor and that it is spreading apart, like the larger Atlantic and Pacific oceans, pushing Arabia apart from Africa. But its narrow width shows that this spreading must have begun relatively recently. It seems that we are witnessing a critical stage in the development of a new ocean and that the Atlantic must have looked similar to the Red Sea as it was splitting Africa and America apart nearly 200 million years ago.

Overleaf: Paricutín volcano, Mexico, active between 1943 and 1952, is an excellent example of a huge cinder cone.

To return to the East African Rift, the very presence of long, major faults either side of a central down-faulted rift suggests that the land on either side of the rift is moving apart. This, coupled with the volcanic activity, is evidence that the rift valley is also a future ocean floor, but at an even earlier stage than the Red Sea. The East African Rift presumably lies over a rising part of the mantle, which will one day split East Africa from the rest of the continent. An ocean floor, similar to the present Red Sea, will then develop which, with basalt eruptions and the creation of new crust, will spread wider and develop a mid-ocean ridge. This is just a possibility, for other overriding forces may come into play which may prevent the spreading of the East African Rift. In that case the rift may remain as a 'failed' ocean or close up again.

There are other areas where similar rifts have tried to develop, or may be in the process of developing. Both France and Germany have recent areas of volcanism which seem to be incipient or failed rifts. The Chaîne des Puys in the Massif Central of France was still erupting when the pyramids of Egypt were built in 4000 BC, extremely recently on the geological scale. This was only the latest of a series of volcanic episodes in this part of France, all of them occurring around the Limagne, apparently some kind of primitive rift system. Some of the earlier episodes produced very big central volcanoes similar to and even larger than Mount Etna, but the Chaîne des Puys was a series of very short-lived, 'one-off' eruptions, sometimes extremely violent, which started about 100,000 years ago and continued until about 5000 years ago. Since there were periods of dormancy 10,000–20,000 years long during this period, it is probable that this region is still in a period of dormancy and activity may recommence in the future.

The continental flood basalts of the United States and other parts of the world are also thought to be at the sites of splitting continents. They are all more than 10 or 20 million years old, so they must represent the sites of failed ocean development, but their appearance is much more like the volcanism characteristic of mid-ocean ridges than that of East Africa. In the Columbia River flood basalts of the United States, enormous quantities of low viscosity (very runny) basaltic lava was erupted in several separate eruptions, travelling great distances and building up huge thicknesses of lava. In places mountains up to 5000 ft (1500 metres) high were submerged beneath the thickness of lava. Each of these eruptions must have been similar to the large extrusions of basalt that occur beneath the sea at mid-ocean ridges.

The other kind of mid-plate volcanism is typified by the Hawaiian Islands in the Pacific. These are thousands of miles from the nearest spreading ridge or subduction zone, yet Kilauea is one of the world's most active volcanoes. Clues to the origin of Hawaiian volcanism are found in the disposition and age of the different islands. They form a chain running southeast to northwest, the same alignment as the direction of motion of the Pacific plate on which they are situated. The oldest islands are found at the northwest end of the chain and the ages become steadily younger towards the southeast, with the highly active Kilauea at the southeastern end of the youngest island. Just northwest of Kilauea lies Mauna Loa, bigger but less active, and beyond that is Hoalalai, which has not erupted for over 100 years. Further south than Kilauea there lies the Loihi Seamount, apparently a volcano on the sea bottom, from which eruptions have been detected by seismic activity, but the top of which still lies nearly 3000 ft (1000 metres) below sea level.

The most likely explanation for these volcanoes is that they each passed over the same 'hot spot' or mantle plume, which remained stationary while the Pacific plate moved above it. The magma generated above the rising mantle plume rose through the oceanic crust to form a volcano, which remained active until the Pacific plate had moved away from the hot spot, cutting off the supply of magma. A new volcano then formed over the hot spot, piercing the plate to the southeast of the old one. From the present activity of Hawaiian volcanoes it is clear that several of them can be active at the same time, the northwesterly ones declining in activity as they gradually move away from the heat source.

While this explanation is not accepted by all volcanologists, it does explain nicely the major features of the Hawaiian chain of volcanic islands. There are also isolated volcanoes in the middle of continental plates which are not part of any well-defined rift system. In the centre of the Sahara, for example, recent volcanic complexes are found which may fall into the same category of volcanism as Hawaii, in that they may also lie over mantle plumes which have succeeded in piercing the continental crust.

4 VOLCANO SHAPE AND SIZE

TYPES OF VOLCANIC VENT

The point at which magma reaches the surface of the Earth and escapes as lava, gas, sublimate and ash is generally known as a *volcanic vent.* Although in popular imagination vents are always thought of as craters, they may in fact be of many different shapes and sizes. The simplest type of vent, sometimes called by its Italian name *bocca* (mouth) is one through which degassed lava escapes quietly without any explosive activity. There is usually some kind of gas escape, however, and when this is very mild, with small explosions in which *spatter* (clots of molten lava) is thrown only a yard or so, these clots solidify immediately around the vent to form a chimney known as a *hornito*, the Spanish word for oven; at night the red glow from these hot vents make this a particularly appropriate name. These chimneys may be less than a yard wide, yet they grow to several feet tall. This makes them rather unstable and they tend to fall after a few years' exposure to the elements.

Where the explosions are rather stronger, the hornito structure is wider and starts to resemble a larger volcanic cone, but the spatter is still molten upon landing, so it sticks together and flattens slightly to make a solid, conical construction along the lines of an irregular stone wall. These are called *spatter cones.*

The most common type of crater formed in this way, known as a *cinder cone*, is constructed from even bigger explosive activity. By the time the ejected clots of lava hit the ground, most have solidified during flight, so the cinder cone consists of a tip of variously sized solid particles of lava with a crater in the middle. Cinder cones are difficult to walk on as the dry particles slide downslope as you step on them, rather like a slag heap or a coal tip. Different proportions of ash are found in cinder cones and if ash predominates, it is sometimes referred to as an *ash cone.* Cinder cones may be as small as 330 ft (100 metres) across at the base and 100 ft (30 metres) high; but they may also be much bigger, like Paricutín in Mexico, which grew to over 1300 ft (400 metres) high and 1 mile (2 km) in diameter between 1943 and 1952. In the bottom of an active cinder cone the actual vent may be seen – a glowing hole a few yards wide from which lava bombs are violently expelled. (A *volcanic bomb* is any large, solid lump thrown out by a volcano.)

The vent of a cinder cone lies at the top of a pipe, usually vertical below ground, so that the explosions are directed upwards, but occasionally inclined pipes occur so that the explosions are directed one way, making that side of the cone higher. A more common cause of this kind of assymmetry is strong wind during the eruption, though if the eruption is mainly ashy, even a comparatively gentle wind will produce a markedly lop-sided cone.

If water is present during the eruption – say the eruption occurs in a shallow lake or near the seashore – the extra pressure from the water flashing to steam causes much bigger explosions. This produces a wider and flatter cone called a *tuff ring*, with a crater often more than ½ mile (1 km) wide, such as Diamond Head crater on the shores of Hawaii, or Hverfjall crater, erupted through a shallow lake at Myvatn, Iceland. Where eruptive activity continues, the tuff ring may grow sufficiently high above the water level that it no longer enters the vent in sufficient quantities for steam explosions to occur. The power of the explosions then diminishes and an ordinary cinder cone forms inside the much wider tuff ring.

Sometimes the presence of water may provoke explosions in which the amount of material thrown out is small compared with the size of the crater. This type of activity simply produces a wide, circular hole in the ground, commonly about ½ mile (1 km) in diameter, known as a *maar.* The crater is usually without any significant rim, or with a rim on one side only where the wind has blown the ejected material – usually fragmented rocks and fine ash from rock pulverized by the explosive activity. Once the eruption has ceased, the crater often fills with water to form a lake or marsh. Many such features are found in the Eifel region of Germany, where the name maar comes from, and also in the Chaîne des Puys in France.

FISSURE ERUPTIONS

So far we have considered types of volcanoes that occur where the magma escapes through a more or less cylindrical, vertical conduit. In practice the upward movement of magma causes the ground to split and

TOP: A hornito is formed from small explosions of lava which is still molten when it lands.
CENTRE: Maars are wide explosion craters formed from steam explosions where ground-water comes into contact with magma.
BOTTOM: Cinder cones are formed when big bubbles of gas in the magma burst, sending showers of lava so high that it solidifies during flight and piles up to form a cone of dry, loose cindery material around the vent.

Types of volcanic vent: external views (left), cross-sections during formation (right).

Floods of lava and clouds of steam pour from part of the Krafla volcano fissure field at Gjastykki, northeast Iceland, in September 1977.

crack so that a cinder cone, for example, usually forms above what was originally a small, elongated crack or fissure. When this fissure is much longer, the vent will not be a simple hole in the ground, but a long slot with magma rising through its entire length. The result is that the familiar, more or less circular crater does not form, but rather a very elongate crater or chain of craters. The fissure has a much larger surface area than an ordinary vent, so the magma can escape much more quickly and fissure eruptions often produce a large volume of lava very rapidly.

The largest fissure eruption to occur in historic time was the Laki Fissure eruption, which began on 8 June 1783. A 15-mile (25-km) length of fissure opened up and lava began to pour out at a colossal rate. Most of the lava flowed down two river valleys, reaching distances of nearly 40 miles (60 km), from the fissure fairly quickly. The lava was very fluid and filled the valleys to depths of 300 ft (100 metres), overflowing some of them. Most of the lavas were erupted in about two months and they were accompanied by strong degassing that produced enormous fountains of lava and a great deal of ash, which blanketed the land, killing crops and spoiling grassland. Many animals also died from gas poisoning. The eruption finished in November, by which time 3 cubic miles (11 cubic km) of lava had been erupted. The eruption devastated agriculture over much of Iceland and nearly a quarter of the island's population died as a result.

The appearance of the Laki Fissure today is typical of this type of eruption. A 15-mile (25-km) line of irregular craters marks the slot along which the lavas were erupted. Some of the craters are elongate along the fissure, others appear as groups or chains of more circular craters and many have one wall breached or missing where the lava has escaped in long channels. Strictly speaking, each of these craters could be regarded as a cinder or spatter cone, but their grouping and their irregular and elongate appearance distinguish the whole structure as a fissure eruption.

Though smaller and less devastating, similar but better-observed fissure eruptions occurred between 1975 and 1984 near Krafla volcano in northern Iceland. This area had not been active for two centuries, but feasibility studies for geothermal power in the 1960s detected a large heat source beneath the volcano that would be ideal for generating electricity. A power station was built, but before it became operational, it was noticed that the building was starting to tilt quite considerably, suggesting that pressure was building up at Krafla. One of the first things to be done following this discovery was the reorganization of the car park so that all the cars would be pointing away from the volcano. Soon afterwards activity began, but luckily not near the power station.

Over the next few years a series of fissure eruptions occurred at intervals of a few months or years. In each case, series of cracks a few miles long opened up and lava poured out, accompanied by long curtains of fountaining lava. The lava was extremely fluid and formed thin flows which spread quickly. The appearance of these flows advancing across snow was quite spectacular, the snow reflecting a delicate, pinkish glow from the curtains of fire. Tilt meters (see p. 146) measuring ground tilt were also able to detect the movement of the magma underground before eruption. The magma was apparently issuing from an underground storage area beneath Krafla, which expanded until vertical cracks propagated north–south beneath the ground. Sometimes nothing else happened, so the magma stayed beneath the ground where it presumably solidified. None the less, the crack usually reached the surface somewhere along its length to create a fissure eruption.

A curious and unique event occurred during one of these episodes when a magma-filled crack was advancing rapidly southwards about ½ mile (1 km) beneath the ground. By chance the subsurface crack hit the bottom of a borehole that had been drilled much earlier as part of the geothermal programme. The magma shot up the narrow hole for several hundred yards and hit the surface, actually producing a tiny fountain of degassing lava for a few minutes before it cooled and sealed the hole. This is the only example of a volcano produced artificially, albeit unwittingly.

COLLAPSE PITS AND CALDERAS

So far we have looked at constructional craters, namely those formed by the piling up of material thrown out from the vent. A different type of crater is formed when the ground subsides, leaving a pit which has no rim and may be markedly non-circular in shape. A subsidence crater of small size is usually referred to as a *collapse pit*. This may form when magma drains from a storage area just beneath the ground, or it may form after an eruption when the surface collapses into a wide vent area.

Summit craters of large and frequently active shield volcanoes are often collapse pits; a good example is the

Collapse pits lie at the summit of Piton de la Fournaise volcano on Reunion Island in the Indian Ocean. Behind can be seen the steep walls of a caldera several miles wide which surrounds the summit cone.

Bocca Nuova at the summit of Mount Etna. Lava filled the wide Central Crater in 1956 and 1964, and tourists were regularly taken along a path that crosses these flows to look at lavas on the northeast side. On 6 June 1968 a glowing hole 23 ft (7 metres) wide suddenly opened on this path between two groups of tourists and gases at over 1000°C began puffing out. This hole was still the same in October 1969 when small gas explosions began, but snow melted around this hole over an area of warm ground 300 ft (100 metres) wide and the inside of the hole could be seen to be overhanging, suggesting that it was just a hole in the roof of a large cavern. This roof collapsed in the winter to leave a steep-sided collapse pit about 300 ft (100 metres) across and 650–1000 ft (200–300 metres) deep. Continued small collapses of sections of the edge enlarged the diameter of the pit to 550 ft (170 metres) in 1978, 850 ft (260 metres) in 1981 and 1000 ft (300 metres) in 1983. At the time of writing the Bocca Nuova is the most active of the summit craters, with explosions occurring deep inside every second or two, although no lavas have yet come from it and no rim of ejected material has formed.

When a similar but much larger withdrawal of magma occurs beneath a volcano, a very wide, steep-sided depression may form known as a *caldera*. This may be quite irregular in shape, depending on the shape of the body of magma that was drained, and can be several miles in diameter. There is no real distinction between a caldera and a collapse pit; a caldera is simply larger. However, the formation of calderas is usually associated with the sudden explosive escape of

magma, often elsewhere on the volcano, so an apparently explosive origin is often assumed, but the non-circular shape and large size of caldera depressions mark them out as primarily subsidence features. The formation of a large caldera is a major event and no one can claim to have seen a caldera collapse at close quarters but observations from a distance in Alaska and the Galapagos Islands suggests that it happens quickly. It is probable that the Krakatoa eruption of 1883 was a caldera-forming event.

Most of the large, persistently active volcanoes have a caldera, or the remains of one, near their summits and some of them have more than one. Each of these calderas represents some crisis point in a volcano's history, such as a large eruption, or a change in stress regime within the volcano, the arrival of a new batch of magma from below or the revival of an old one. Mount Etna has traces of two old calderas measuring 2 × 2½ miles (3 × 4 km), long since filled in with lavas and cones, and Kilauea and Mauna Loa both have comparatively recent ones, also elongated and about 2 × 3 miles (3 × 4.5 km) wide with steep cliffs.

LARGE, PERSISTENTLY ACTIVE VOLCANOES

Many volcanoes are the result of only one eruption, which may last from a few days to a few years, after which the vent appears to seal itself up. No further activity ever occurs at that location again, though other similar eruptions may occur nearby. Paricutín, Mexico, the volcanoes of the Chaîne des Puys, France, and many of the Icelandic volcanoes are probably of this

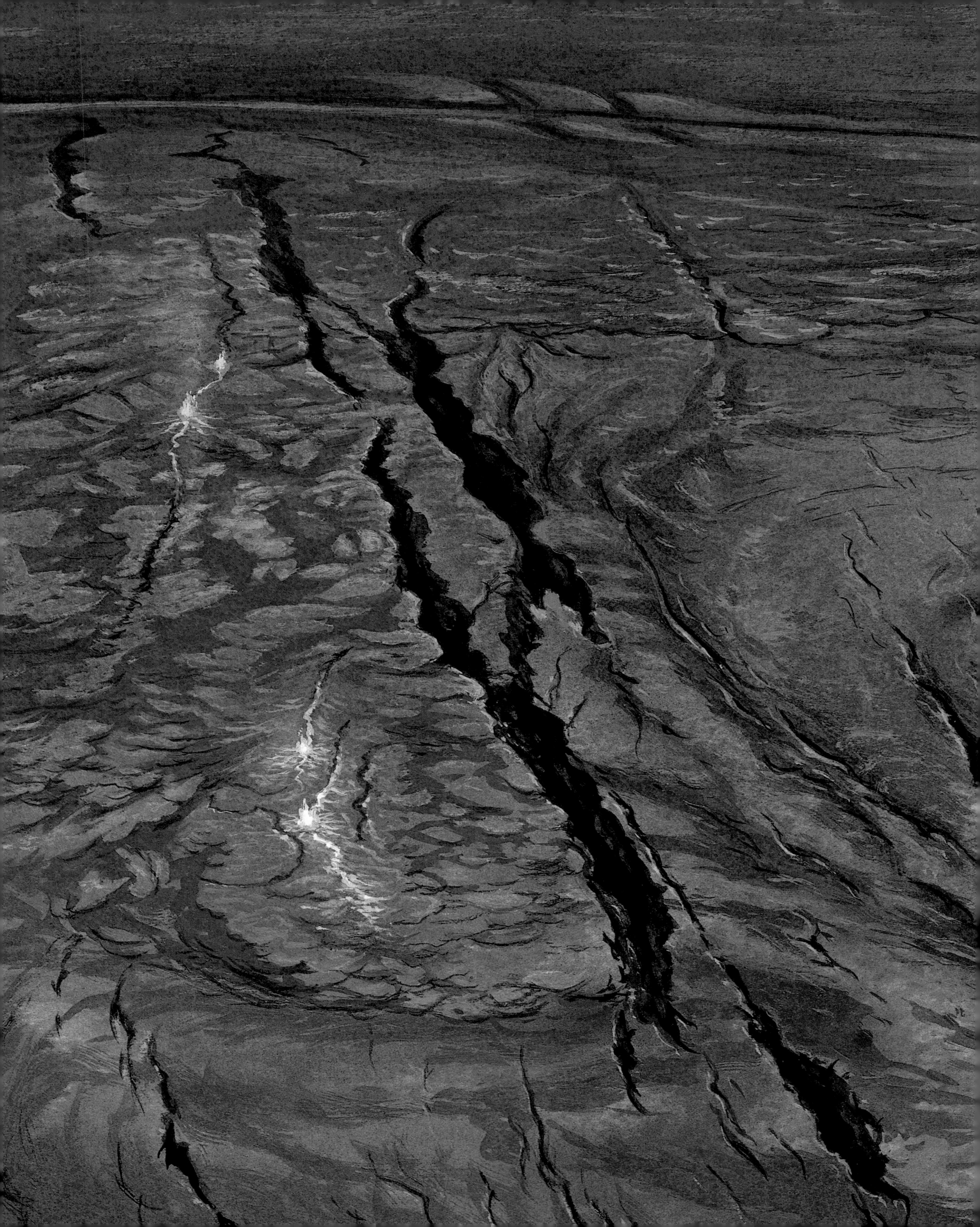

Gaping cracks and fissures on the southwest rift zone of Kilauea volcano, Hawaii. Lava fountains erupt from some parts of the rift zone.

type. Other volcanoes are just the opposite. Once volcanic activity has started, it seems unable to stop and continues to produce eruptions over tens or hundreds of thousands of years until a huge structure is built up which may be thousands of feet high and tens of miles wide. Etna, Kilauea, Mount Fuji, Popocatepetl, Nyaragongo, Mount Erebus and Cotopaxi all fall into this category.

These big volcanoes are usually classified according to their shape. *Shield volcanoes*, such as Kilauea and Mauna Loa on Hawaii, have very shallow slopes (angled at less than 5 degrees) formed by the successive eruption of fluid lavas which flow far before solidifying, so do not build up steep slopes around the central vent. They resemble a shield lying flat on the ground, which may be circular or elongated if the lavas are also erupted from fissure systems across the summit, as happens on Hawaii. Although the slopes of these volcanoes are shallow, the persistent eruptions may build them up to great heights. The summit of Mauna Loa is 13,000 ft (4000 metres) above sea level, but it has also built up from the sea bottom 16,000 ft (5000 metres) below, so that the total thickness of accumulated lavas is more than 29,000 ft (9000 metres) – higher than Mount Everest.

Steeper-sided volcanoes are usually built up from less fluid lavas, which cannot spread so far. These more viscous lavas are also associated with more explosive types of eruption, so layers of ash and other ejected material alternate with the layers of lava within the volcano. This type of volcano is known as a *strato volcano* or a *composite volcano* and is the classic, conically-shaped volcano with a crater at the top that springs to most people's minds when the word volcano is mentioned.

Once the volcano has grown big enough, rising magma within it before an eruption may find it easier to fracture the slopes of the volcano and make a new crater there. The slopes of large shield and strato volcanoes are therefore usually covered with these *flank* or '*parasitic*' *cones* and craters, which may account for up to half the eruptions of a large volcano.

Flank eruptions produce not only parasitic craters, but also large volumes of lava, which when solidified will produce higher topography on the side of the volcano from which they flow. Flank eruptions tend to occur along weaknesses in the volcanic edifice, so certain sides of the volcano will have more flank eruptions than others and the repeated eruptions will build up a ridge on this side, making the shape of the volcano elongated in that direction. Flank eruptions then occur along the top of the ridge, known as a *volcanic rift zone*, similar in some ways to the large rift systems found in East Africa or Iceland, but on a much smaller scale. The rift zones on the large Hawaiian volcanoes are up to 60 miles (100 km) long, but only 10 miles (15 km) long on Mount Etna.

As there is no law to restrict the size of volcanoes, the continued upbuilding of large, persistently active volcanoes, particularly strato volcanoes, results in the top becoming too steep, too high and ultimately unstable. The same problem occurs with snow and ice on high mountains above the snowline – the continued snowfall means that the ice-cap gets thicker and thicker. Luckily ice can flow, so glaciers remove the excess ice as fast as it accumulates. Solid rock and ash cannot flow at this rate, so a continually erupting volcano inevitably becomes too steep.

The result is either caldera collapse, where the summit collapses into the molten magma beneath, or else catastrophic slope failure, a broad term including landslides, rockslides and rock avalanches. Known as *sector collapse* on a volcano, a large sector of the slope, which may include the summit, peels off and slides downslope off the volcano. Large volumes of magma beneath the surface may then be laid open to the atmosphere, provoking immediate degassing and a gigantic explosive eruption. The best known recent example of this type of activity was the eruption of Mount St Helens on 18 May 1980 (see pp 118–19). However, the tell-tale steep, amphitheatre-shaped valleys of sector collapses, sometimes called *avalanche calderas*, can be seen on the sides of many large volcanoes, such as Mount Etna, Piton de la Fournaise and Nevado de Colima. Apart from Mount St Helens, sector collapses have occurred historically at Bandai San, Japan, in 1888, and at Bezymianny volcano, Kamchatka, in 1956 (see p. 112).

DOMES, SPINES AND TABLE MOUNTAINS

Whereas basaltic magma normally erupts as fairly fluid lava, the more silica-rich types of magma found near destructive plate margins are frequently much more viscous (solid or pasty), producing a very different type of volcano. The magma is pushed up through the volcano like toothpaste through a tube and the process can be extremely slow. Instead of liquid lava pouring out of a crater, this type of volcano often has a rounded top known as a *dome*, where the lava is rising up as a

Kluchevsko volcano, Kamchatka, a fine example of a large volcano with several parasitic cones down its flanks.

The famous spine of Mount Pelée at its highest in May 1903. This column of lava was pushed up slowly like toothpaste until it was 1000 feet (300 metres) high, but as it cooled, it gradually cracked and crumbled into a pile of rocks.

solid mass which may be several hundred yards wide. There is virtually no flow from this dome, but sections of the edge peel off when it gets too steep and roll down the slopes on either side.

Colima volcano in Mexico has been erupting in this way since 1960, but even when viewed from the top, it is difficult to tell that it is in eruption. The only clues are the hot fumaroles (see p. 70) in the dome at the top, which slowly release volcanic gases which drift downwind, and the small avalanches which occur about every twenty minutes down the steepest side of the volcano, where hot rocks from the rising dome break away and roll downslope. From year to year, however, the top of the volcano can be seen to be slowly evolving as the lava dome rises and crumbles away. Occasionally slightly more fluid lava is erupted, which forms very thick, block lava flows (see p. 73) which creep a few hundred yards downslope before coming to a halt. Sometimes eruptions of this type can continue for more than fifty years. The only excitement is when a particularly large section of the dome peels off, suddenly laying bare a sizeable area of magma which then releases its gas very explosively as a small nuée ardente (see p. 15), similar to those that issued from Mount Pelée in 1902.

Sometimes the dome being squeezed out may be narrow and rise more rapidly to form a narrow tower known as a *spine*. The best known and most spectacular spine was that which rose from Mount Pelée at the end of its devastating 1902 eruption. In November of that year a dome began to push its way up out of the volcano at a rate of several yards a day, so that by May 1903 it was more than 1000 ft (300 metres) high – higher than the Eiffel Tower. However, as soon as it began to cool, it cracked and collapsed, so by the end of the year this spectacular monument had become an ignominious pile of rocks.

A slightly different type of dome has been produced from Usu volcano, Japan, in 1910 and 1943. In these eruptions the extremely viscous magma did not break the surface but simply pushed it up from below. The 1943 eruption was better documented, thanks to the postmaster of a nearby village, who periodically sketched the skyline towards Usu from his window. An area of land about 2 miles (3 km) across, which included a village, began to rise slowly and by October 1944 had risen some 500 ft (150 metres). In November a column of glowing lava finally appeared in the centre of the area, rising eventually to 1000 ft (300 metres) above the original ground surface. However, the column of lava was still capped by mud and clay, now considerably baked, of the original ground surface that it had taken up with it.

Steep-sided or flat-topped volcanoes of a completely different type are the *table mountains* of Iceland. As we have seen, Icelandic eruptions are usually the site of extremely fluid lavas and these table mountains are no exception. They consist of horizontal layers of fluid basalt lava, but the volcanoes are only a few miles wide, sometimes much less, and are surrounded by steep cliffs. These volcanoes are all several thousand years old and were formed from volcanic eruptions under the thick ice-cap that covered Iceland during the last Ice Age. The lava was able to melt the ice in its immediate vicinity, but the ice rapidly cooled the lava so that it did not flow very far, and the succeeding eruptions, also similarly limited in lateral extent, built up horizontal layers of lava above it. When the volcano built up to the surface of the ice-cap, a normal subaerial volcano was superimposed on the subglacial one.

When the ice-caps melted at the end of the Ice Age, these curiously steep-sided and flat-topped volcanoes were exposed. There is at present a subglacial active volcano, Grimsvötn, beneath the large ice-cap of Vatnajökull in southern Iceland, which, if global warming continues, may itself become a table mountain some time in the future.

UNDERWATER VOLCANOES

Although we cannot see them, there must be large numbers of unknown active volcanoes beneath the sea at mid-ocean ridges and other submerged sites of volcanic activity. Volcanic eruptions which poke just above sea level have been reported in ship's logbooks for centuries, though the physical evidence is usually washed away by waves within a few weeks or months of the eruption. The most famous such eruption in recent years was Surtsey, which appeared off the coast of Iceland in 1963. However, there are many volcanoes much deeper down in the ocean which are only now being discovered through painstaking exploration in small submarines.

Of the many difficulties encountered in exploring an underwater volcano, particularly one in eruption, is the problem of limited visibility – often only a few

The table mountain of Mount Herthubreith, Iceland. The shape of this volcano is the result of eruptions under an ice sheet which limited the flow of lava to produce the high, steep cliffs around the 'table top'.

LEFT: *Lava flowing beneath the sea. The zigzag line of red is where lava is oozing out of a crack before being rapidly chilled by the water.* ABOVE: *A 'black smoker'. Gas and ash pour out of a vent in a volcanically active area beneath the sea.*

yards in dark, murky waters. Nevertheless, the sites of gas emission are immediately obvious from the myriad bubbles that rise from them, and some vigorous sites, known as *black smokers*, send out thick, dark clouds of ash as well.

Lava erupting under water is a particularly spectacular sight. Like the ice in subglacial volcanoes, water cools the lava very quickly, so it cannot flow very far. The surface appears dark until, suddenly, a new red-hot driblet of lava races out from the mass to cool rapidly and darken, sometimes rolling downslope, to be followed by another batch of lava rapidly extruded in the same way. These separate batches are very characteristic of lava erupted under water, and where upheavals have brought old underwater flows above sea level, the separate, rounded batches of lava look like sections through plump pillows, hence their name *pillow lavas*.

OVERLEAF: *A volcanic eruption breaks the surface off the coast of Iceland in 1963 to form a new island, later named Surtsey.*

The volcano Stromboli, in the Mediterranean Sea, has been known since ancient times as the 'Lighthouse of the Mediterranean' because of the persistence and reliability of its eruptions.

5
TYPES OF ERUPTION

FIRE FOUNTAINING AND STROMBOLIAN ACTIVITY

A volcanic eruption occurs when magma reaches the Earth's surface. Although this may manifest itself in different ways, all types of eruption have certain things in common. In each case the magma has been under considerable pressure deep beneath the Earth from the great weight of overlying rocks, but as it rises towards the surface, the pressure drops and on eruption it virtually ceases altogether.

All magma types have considerable amounts of gas in them, which, while deep inside the Earth, are kept dissolved in the magma by pressure. However, as the magma nears the surface, the gases expand to form bubbles in the magma and separate from it on eruption. The same kind of phenomenon can be seen when you unscrew the top of any fizzy drink. Before unscrewing, the bottle is sealed, the high pressure on the liquid inside does not change, so the liquid appears flat, despite the fact that it has carbon dioxide gas dissolved in it. As soon as the top is unscrewed, however, the pressure on the liquid drops suddenly and the gas within it starts to expand, seen as bubbles forming and rising steadily to the surface. The expansion occurs because the pressure is less near the top of the liquid. The same thing happens within magma inside a volcano. The rising, expanding gas bubbles take up more room, pushing the magma out at a faster speed. It is the gas within a magma that is the main driving force in a volcanic eruption.

The simplest type of eruptive activity is *fire fountaining*. This occurs in very fluid lavas erupted at a high rate and is common in Iceland and Hawaii. The expanding gas projects the lavas high into the air as a continuous fountain. If it is a fissure eruption, a spectacular curtain of fire forms from which the lava races away in fiery red channels. The noise of a fire fountain consists not only of the gas hissing as the lava is thrown out, but also a clinkery tinkling, for the highest lumps of ejected lava solidify during flight and can be heard as they hit the ground. Fire fountains can vary greatly in height, the highest ever recorded being produced during the 1959 eruption of Kilauea, when fountains reached 1900 ft (580 metres) high.

A slightly different type of activity is observed at Stromboli volcano, one of the Aeolian Islands off the northeast coast of Sicily. This has been fairly continuously active since Roman times and is known as the 'lighthouse of the Mediterranean' from the reliability of its eruptions. Its craters do not have the continuous fountains of the Hawaiian eruptions, but similar clots of liquid lava are thrown out in distinct explosions, which may vary in frequency from every few seconds to every few hours, depending on the state of the volcano. This is known as *strombolian activity* and can be seen at many other volcanoes around the world. It usually occurs where the lavas are slightly more viscous (stiffer) and the eruptive rate not so high. The expanding gas within the magma collects into quite large-sized bubbles which can be a few yards across. As these reach the surface, they burst, sometimes with a bang, producing the characteristic strombolian explosion and showering molten lava into the air. As lava is not flowing from the craters at Stromboli most of the time, the lava at the bottom of the craters may remain molten for months or years, with an explosion every now and then as a fresh bubble of gas sluggishly reaches the surface and bursts.

Strombolian activity at night is one of the most beautiful and awe-inspiring sights of nature, particularly if it is safe to climb to the edge of the crater and look in. The glowing vent can be seen calmly fuming away until suddenly a brilliant red flash heralds a huge shower of bright red lava bombs. These rise high into the air, each one deforming and changing shape as it rises, then seeming to hang in the air before descending in a perfect parabolic curve and smacking into the ground. A characteristic 'woomph' may accompany the explosion, and in strong ones the air shock can be seen passing through the shower of lava; observers feel it hit them a fraction of a second later. Sometimes much louder bangs occur, often with very little matter ejected, presumably the sound of trapped gases escaping and burning explosively.

The size of explosions and the interval between them varies greatly and cannot be relied on to guage safety; indeed, doing so has been the cause of many deaths at Stromboli and other volcanoes. The temptation to stay all night at the crater edge is strong, but one can never be sure that a very much bigger explosion will not

LEFT: The Myvatn area of Iceland as it may have looked some 3800 years ago when a lava flow from the Kefildyngja shield volcano flowed over an area of meres and marshes. Dozens of pseudocraters formed as trapped water vaporized explosively beneath the hot lava.

occur. When the interval between explosions is an hour or so, adventurous tourists have been tempted to nip down inside the crater immediately after an explosion to pick up a fresh lava bomb, only to be fatally surprised by another explosion a minute or two later.

PHREATOMAGMATIC AND PHREATIC ACTIVITY

If water is present and becomes mixed with magmatic material during eruption, ordinary fire fountaining or strombolian activity, which is comparatively safe to watch from a certain distance, can suddenly become extremely violent. Paradoxically, this type of explosive outburst often begins during a lull in activity when tourists are particularly likely to venture too close.

Perhaps the best known activity of this type occurred on Hawaii in May 1924. Kilauea volcano is normally one of the safest types, with lava fountaining being the dominant type of eruptive activity and ample warning of eruption being given in the form of local earthquakes and ground-cracking. However, in the early months of 1924 the usual red-hot lava lake inside Halemaumau, the collapse pit within the summit caldera, began to drain away until the floor of the crater was visible. Collapse of the crater floor then showed that the magma level was still continuing to drop hundreds of feet below its usual level.

Suddenly, in early May, a series of powerful steam explosions began, sending huge clouds of ash up to 1 mile (2 km) high and hurling blocks weighing several tons hundreds of yards from the crater. The sudden lowering of the magma level to below the water table, and the cracking that accompanied it, meant that the ground-water was able to mix with the magma and the hot rocks of the crater walls, where it apparently became trapped in some places, causing its conversion to steam. The resulting explosive episodes lasted from a few minutes to several hours and one photographer who got too close was hit by a falling rock and killed. This phase of activity lasted for two and a half weeks before Kilauea became its normal calmer self again.

Phreatomagmatic activity, in which steam and magmatic gases both contribute to the force of the explosions, is most obvious in eruptions that start beneath the sea and build up craters that break the surface. Surtsey, which appeared off the coast of Iceland in 1963, is the best known recent eruption of this type. Had the eruption occurred on dry land, fire fountaining would have been the dominant type of activity. However, the constant mixing of the erupting magma with sea water meant that its surface was cooled rapidly so that a solid crust would form which would then burst explosively every few seconds. In addition, the constant trapping of water meant that there was a much higher steam content in the gases that were expelled, producing bigger explosions that fragmented the lava into black ash. The result was the 'cock's tail' or 'cypressoid' appearance of the explosion, in which the 'cauliflower' of white steam contrasts with the shower of black ash streamers which burst through it. Every so often, much longer episodes of continuous explosive expulsion occurred, building up huge columns of ash and producing a continuous rain of lava blocks, which splashed into the sea like huge hailstones.

Steam explosions are called *phreatic* when no mixing with fresh magma is involved. They are all the more dangerous because they do not always occur during eruptions, so they can be completely unexpected. A tragic explosion of this type occurred at the summit of Mount Etna in September 1979. There had been some heavy rain in the last week of August, then on 2 September a rain-sodden section of the inside walls of the Bocca Nuova, one of the summit craters, slipped down to block the vent on the floor of the crater. Over the next ten days the heat from below slowly made its way through the wet, slumped material, gradually raising the temperature at the base to above 100°C. The pressure of the wet blockage did not allow the water to boil, so a large amount of the water became superheated. When the pressure was finally overcome, all the water flashed to steam in a single large explosion in the late afternoon of 12 September. As it was a fine day and the crater was not active, there were around 150 tourists standing on the edge when it went up. Altogether, thirty of them were hit by falling rocks and stones, and nine were killed.

Phreatic explosions may also occur where advancing lavas flow over snow or bodies of water. This frequently happens when a house is overrun by lava; the water tank can be heated up beneath the flow until it vaporizes and explodes. A flow advancing into a lake or the sea can be spectacular to watch from a distance, but at the foot of Mount Etna in 1842 a lava flow advancing into a lake near the town of Brontë killed nine local spectators in one enormous steam blast.

A similar series of explosions must also have taken place at Skutustadir, Iceland, where a flow advancing into Lake Myvatn has produced a series of beautifully symmetrical 'pseudocraters'. These are so called be-

PREVIOUS PAGE: *Nuées ardentes pour rapidly down the sides of Mount Mayon in the Philippines in 1968.*

BELOW: *Views of Mount St Helens volcano before and after the catastrophic sector collapse of 18 May 1980.*

cause they look like ordinary strombolian cones, but are actually the result of trapped lake water exploding beneath the flow and have no volcanic roots.

NUÉES ARDENTES, SECTOR COLLAPSES AND IGNIMBRITES

One of the most dangerous of all volcanic phenomena is the nuée ardente (see p. 15), illustrated on pages 64–5. First recognized and described during the 1902 eruption of Mount Pelée in Martinique, nuées are capable of killing everything within an area of several square miles in only a few minutes. The recent deaths of forty-one people at Mount Unzen, Japan, were caused by a nuée. Most are associated with gas-rich, viscous magma and are usually initiated by a huge and powerful explosion. This ejects enormous quantities of lava in sizes ranging from blocks several yards across right down to fine ash. The thick, ashy cloud rapidly expands upwards, but at a certain moment the base of the cloud starts to extend rapidly downhill, flowing like a grey, turbulent liquid. This is the nuée ardente itself, and as it progresses downslope and thins out, it runs down the valleys only, but all the time sending up thick, dark clouds of ash which rapidly rise in cauliflower-like convolutions of dust and ash. At night these dense clouds can be seen to be filled with incandescent material.

The whole phenomenon is often likened to a well-shaken fizzy drink. English volcanologists usually talk in terms of the uninspiring bottle of beer; I prefer the French analogy of opening a bottle of champagne. If the cork is released suddenly, there is a loud detonation and the cork flies out followed by a fine spray of champagne; this is like the initial explosion and the cloud of rocks and fine ash ejected. Shortly after, the rapidly degassing champagne rises up the bottle, overflows as expanding froth and pours down the sides. If poured into a glass, it continues degassing inside the glass, producing more froth that may also overflow the sides. The froth is like the nuée ardente, but there is an important difference.

A real nuée is not a liquid, but consists of a dense cloud of very hot gas, dust, ash, lumps of lava and even big boulders, but the cloud is so dense, thick and charged with gas that it is able to flow like water downslope and thus cover enormous distances in a very short time. This kind of gas-lubricated dry flow which makes accumulations of solid particles flow like a fluid is called *fluidization* and is extensively used in industry to move powders through tubes for packaging. The mobility of a nuée ardente is helped by the fact that every single lump of lava ejected continues to expand and give off jets of gas as it is carried downslope, so each particle is like a little hovercraft riding on a cushion of gas. Air trapped beneath the nuée also helps it to glide downslope easily, and the gas streaming out of each particle keeps it from colliding with others within the cloud, lowering friction still further. Another result of this gas cushioning is that the nuée itself is almost silent, eerily rushing downhill with the force of a hurricane, giving no warning to anything in its path. The nuée that hit St Pierre in 1902 was able to melt glass, so temperatures within the cloud must have been 600°–700°C, making it instantly lethal.

The nuée ardente was the first type of fluidized volcanic flow to be described, but since that time other types of fluidization phenomena, collectively known as *pyroclastic flows*, have been recognized, both bigger and smaller than the 'classic' nuée. One of these is called *base surge* and may develop at the base of an explosive, eruptive column when it is particularly large. However, it can also develop during any large explosion and is particularly noticeable in nuclear explosions. Base surge deposits have even been recognized around large impact craters on the Moon. They can be seen as ground-hugging clouds racing out from the base of explosions and may be initiated by *column collapse*, where the mass of material ejected upwards from the crater becomes too voluminous and too dense and starts to collapse catastrophically as the material falls back to Earth. The resulting expelled gas, dust and boulders rush outward and flow downhill as a fluidized flow. Base surge clouds were prominent during the 1951 eruption of Mount Lamington (see p. 112), which devastated a huge area and killed nearly 3000 people.

Fluidized flow may become particularly important during sector collapse, when a major landslide removes a large part of the slope of a steep-sided volcano. This happened to Bandai San volcano, Japan, in 1888, and to Bezymianny volcano in the USSR, on 30 March 1956, but the best known example of this type was the much-photographed eruption of Mount St Helens, Washington, on 18 May 1980. In these last two eruptions the volcanoes concerned had been in intermittent activity for weeks, causing a large area on one side of the volcano to become unstable until, suddenly, the entire slope began to detach itself and slide off the mountain. In both cases the summit of the volcano was involved in the slide.

The Valley of Ten Thousand Smokes as it appeared when first discovered in 1916. It was formed by an ignimbrite, the most violent and destructive type of eruptive activity known on Earth, which filled the valley of the Ukak River during the 1912 eruption of Mount Katmai.

The effect was rather akin to taking the lid off a pressure cooker, for the gas-rich magma beneath, kept under pressure by the overburden, was suddenly revealed. Immediately, millions of cubic yards of magma began degassing explosively at once, causing the most colossal blast and blowing millions of tons of fine ash and gas-charged rocks into the atmosphere. The amount of material ejected, and the rapidity with which it was done, meant that a huge pyroclastic flow poured down the mountain after the landslide and rapidly overtook it, behaving much as a gigantic nuée and devastating the country. In the case of Bezymianny it travelled 15 miles (24 km), while with Mount St Helens it travelled 12 miles (20 km). Recent studies of Krakatoa have suggested that sector collapse, or possibly caldera collapse, may also have taken place here during the 1883 eruption, but partly underwater which added a phreatic element to the violence and caused many of the tsunamis.

The most devastating type of pyroclastic flow, in fact the most powerful eruptions known on Earth, form *ignimbrites*. Only one of these is definitely known to have formed in historic time – that of the Valley of Ten Thousand Smokes (see p. 109), which came from near Mount Katmai in Alaska in 1912. However, the Krakatoa eruption may also have a released an ignimbrite under water. The Mount Katmai eruption produced 2 cubic miles (10 cubic km) of ignimbrite, but this was a pretty tame affair compared to some prehistoric ignimbrites.

Although it is not yet clear how the different types of ignimbrite are formed, they all exhibit several common features. All are of large volume and were formed very quickly; most are associated with caldera collapse; and most owe their large volume and high eruption rate to the fact that they came out of long fissures rather than vents, which allowed a much larger volume of magma to escape.

The largest and most violent eruptions known on Earth are all prehistoric ignimbrites. To give an idea of the scale that must have been involved in these ancient eruptions, it has been calculated that one which took place in AD 186 in the Taupo valley, New Zealand, was at one stage erupting at the almost unthinkable rate of 3 cubic miles (15 cubic km) of magma per minute. In the San Juan volcanic province in New Mexico, USA, there is an ignimbrite deposit 28 million years old which has a volume estimated at about 700 cubic miles (3000 cubic km).

FUMAROLES, GEYSERS AND HOT SPRINGS

Eruptions which produce ignimbrites are the most powerful volcanic phenomena. By way of contrast, fumaroles, geysers and hot springs are the least powerful manifestations of volcanic activity and may persist for hundreds of thousands of years after a volcanic region has become extinct.

A *fumarole*, sometimes called a *solfatara* after a long-lived area of fumaroles in the Phlegrean Fields, near Naples, Italy, is a general term for a hole or small area of ground persistently giving off steam, gas or sublimates. On dormant volcanoes they can be useful indicators of the general state of things. An increase in fumarole temperatures or the appearance of new fumaroles are sometimes the first indicators of a new eruption. However, these are not infallible indicators; unrelated changes within the volcano may mean that both these signs occur without any subsequent eruption.

Fumaroles mark the point where cracks or other weaknesses within the volcano meet the ground surface. The commonest type of fumarole, which is usually short-lived, consists of a warm hole emitting steam. In this case the weakness does not extend deep within the volcano, but to a depth at which the ground temperatures are considerably higher than the surface, so ground-water, or rain-water percolating through, will be heated and the vapour will escape up the crack.

More active and persistent fumaroles, in which magmatic gases such as sulphur dioxide, hydrogen chloride or hydrogen sulphide escape, come from cracks which penetrate close to a body of magma beneath the ground. They often have brightly coloured deposits of sulphur or other sublimates collecting around them. Even if the magma body beneath the ground has ceased to be active and is cooling, it may continue to give off gas and sublimates for tens or hundreds of years, especially if it is deeply buried, but the sudden appearance of new fumaroles with rapidly increasing magmatic gas output indicates that an eruption is likely.

Geysers are vents where boiling water and steam periodically spout up from the ground in an outburst lasting from a few seconds to a minute or so. The heights attained by these outbursts can (exceptionally) reach thousands of feet and the time interval between them varies from a few minutes to a few hours, depending on the individual geyser. They are much rarer than fumaroles, occurring at small localities in current or previously active volcanic areas. The best known ones are in the western United States, New Zealand, Chile and at Geysir in Iceland, from where the name derives. Geysers are temporary features and some of the spectacular ones in New Zealand and Iceland have now ceased to be active, but others have taken their place.

In structure, geysers appear to be similar to fumaroles in that both are weaknesses or cracks which extend down to much hotter areas beneath. Geysers, however, occur in areas where there is a considerable supply of underground water and where temperatures exceed boiling point relatively near the surface. The geyser conduit fills with ground-water which is steadily heated from below. The water at the bottom of the conduit therefore reaches 100°C first, but is prevented from boiling by the hydrostatic pressure of the column of water above it. It continues to heat up, becoming considerably superheated until, finally, it boils. As soon as this happens, it pushes up the water above, relieving pressure throughout the column of water which all suddenly boils at once, shooting up the conduit and blowing out of the top. The water then starts to collect in the conduit again and the process is repeated. The hot water dissolves all sorts of minerals from the rocks over the years and these are deposited around the mouth of the geyser, often in beautifully subtle shades of colour, but continued deposition eventually narrows and seals up the shaft. Geyser-type activity, or *geysering*, may also occur in volcanoes which have crater lakes, such as Poás in Costa Rica, where there has been intermittent geysering for a number of years.

Hot springs are the last signs of volcanic activity to persist and are still found in the Massif Central, France, where the last volcano erupted 5000 years ago, and in the Eifel district of Germany. They are the result of underground water being heated by buried magma and on an active volcano may vary in temperature according to activity. Springs may also be abruptly cut off after an eruption if subsurface injection of magma cuts off the supply, or if new faulting opens up an easier route for the ground-water. Hot springs, like geysers, dissolve minerals more easily than cold springs and in some regions the high mineral content was held to be good for the health. During the nineteenth century especially, spa towns and health resorts grew up around hot springs at many places in Europe.

A geyser at Geysir, Iceland, sending a jet of superheated water 100 feet (30 metres) into the air.

Types of lava surface: (from top to bottom) Aa; Pahoehoe (in a lava tube); Block lava.

6 VOLCANIC PRODUCTS

TYPES OF LAVA SURFACE

The two most common types of surface found on lava flows are called *pahoehoe* (pronounced 'pah-hoy-hoy') and *aa* (pronounced 'ah-ah'). Both names are Hawaiian words and are reputed to be the sounds made by those walking barefoot across these flows. Pahoehoe is smooth, undulating or ropy in texture and like solid rock to walk on, whereas aa is rough, sharp and consists of loose lumps; like a slag heap or pile or coal, it moves easily when walked on.

It is hard to describe just how difficult, uncomfortable and even dangerous walking across a fresh aa flow can be. You cannot trust any foothold and if you disturb some of the big blocks that make up the surface of the flow, you are liable to bring down bone-crushing boulders. Should you fall over a block, you will soon notice that it is covered with angular edges and needle-sharp spines, so the exercise is not unlike walking over piles of broken glass: clothes and hands are torn to shreds.

Underneath this loose, rubbly surface, however, which is only about 3 ft (1 metre) thick, the centre of the flow consists of plastic, massive lava that forms solid rock when it cools.

There is no chemical difference between pahoehoe and aa lava, despite the great difference in texture. Both occur in basaltic lava, which is composed of about half silica and flows easily. Basalt flows usually consist of areas of both pahoehoe and aa, though the relative proportions of each will vary greatly from volcano to volcano and even from eruption to eruption. Many flows have pahoehoe surfaces near the vent, which change to aa further down the flow as the lava cools, though tongues of pahoehoe lava may appear in the middle of an aa flow.

The causes of the differences between the two lie in the relationship between the viscosity (stiffness) of the lava and the rate at which it is being pushed and deformed – usually dependent on the eruption rate. A flow may emerge hot, beginning to solidify and become more viscous (stiffer) as it cools. The continued pressure of the erupting lava will break up the pahoehoe surface into smaller, solid lumps, which build up the rubbly surface characteristic of an aa flow. Similarly, if two flows erupt at different rates but at the same temperature and viscosity, the slower flow may remain as pahoehoe while the faster one is broken up into aa due to the higher pressure of the erupting lava.

Basalt lava flows of both pahoehoe and aa-type form *lava channels* and tunnels called *lava tubes* as they grow. Soon after the eruption has begun, much of the flow has become fairly stationary and movement is already restricted to a few well-defined rivers of lava, called lava channels, which carry the molten lava from the vent to the advancing flow front. As the eruption continues, the surface of these flowing rivers of lava may freeze over to form a roof of solid basalt enclosing the flow beneath in a tunnel or lava tube. This roof then insulates the lava so that it can continue to flow much further before solidifying. Once the eruption has stopped, the lava flows out of the lava tubes to leave a series of caves and tunnels that mark the underground distributary system of the active flow. Lava tubes vary in size from small ones less than 3 ft (1 metre) wide and a few yards long right up to large tubes with galleries several yards wide and lengths of several miles.

A third type of lava surface, called *block lava*, is found where the viscosity of the lava is higher. Although named differently, there is in fact a continuous gradation between aa and block lava. This type is characteristic of more acidic (higher-silica-content) volcanoes and good examples are found at Colima, Mexico, and Lassen Peak, USA, in association with dome formation. The lava consists of lumps up to a few yards across, much bigger than an aa flow. They are made of massive lava that has formed comparatively clean fractures, and individual blocks may be almost cubic in shape.

Lava flows can be of any volume up to several cubic miles, but the distance travelled by the flow will depend upon the viscosity and the rate at which it is erupted. Low viscosity basalt flows erupted at a high rate will flow the furthest and a good example is the 1783 Laki Fissure eruption in Iceland, which had a volume of about 3 cubic miles (11 cubic km) erupted at a rate of around 27,000 cubic ft (800 cubic metres) per second. It reached distances of over 35 miles (56 km). By contrast, the largest *dacite* (very acidic) flow known, the Chao lava in northern Chile, which has a volume of 6 cubic miles (24 cubic km) flowed only

Light curtains of ash (left) can be seen falling out of the eruptive cloud over Surtslinger, a small vent which appeared out of the sea near Surtsey, Iceland, in 1965. Much heavier falls of ash can occur during violent eruptions, causing extensive damage to crops and livestock, and even causing suffocation.

6 miles (10 km) because of its low viscosity. This lava flow, which must have erupted extremely slowly, has piled up close to the vent to thicknesses approaching 2500 ft (800 metres).

ASHFALLS AND FLOWS

Any violent activity of a volcano involves the fragmentation of magma and wall rocks into tiny particles known as *volcanic ash*. The difference from ordinary ash, which is the residue of oxidation caused by fire, should be emphasized. Nothing burns in a volcanic crater except gases. Volcanic ash consists of rock particles, authority having decreed that any volcanic fragments smaller than ⅕ in (4 mm) in diameter shall be known as ashes. During strombolian activity, the amount of ash produced is small and can only be detected if you happen to be standing downwind of the crater; then your head will start to itch from the ash particles that fall out of the eruption plume from time to time.

Volcanic eruptions are sometimes classified according to their violence, with *hawaiian eruptions* (fire fountains) being the quietest, followed in increasing order of violence by *strombolian*, *vulcanian* and *plinian eruptions*. Generally speaking, the more violent the activity, the more ash produced. Thus, in vulcanian eruptions (see p. 107) thick, dark curtains of ash can be seen drifting out of the cauliflower-shaped eruption plume as it drifts downwind. Plinian eruptions can produce devastating falls of ash that may become many feet thick in a very short time. A typical plinian example is the AD 79 eruption of Vesuvius (see pp 97–105), in which so much ash fell so quickly that the inhabitants of Pompeii had no time to get away and were buried alive.

Deposition of ash may be quite widespread and *ashfalls* from large eruptions, such as Hekla volcano in Iceland, which covered most of the island to depths of a few inches, provide useful dating horizons in archaeological as well as geological investigations.

Sometimes, electric charges built up in the eruption cloud may cause particles of ash to stick together in little balls. These are called *ash hailstones* or *accretionary lapilli* and measure about an inch in diameter.

A pyroclastic flow (see p. 67) or *ash flow* is a general name covering any fluidized mass containing ash, rocks and gas that swoops down a volcano as a ground-hugging flow. The term also includes nuées ardentes and ignimbrites (see pp 15 and 69).

Volcanic bombs: (from top) Cowpat; Spindle; Breadcrust; Ribbon; Pélé's Tears. The last are about actual size; the rest are reduced in scale.

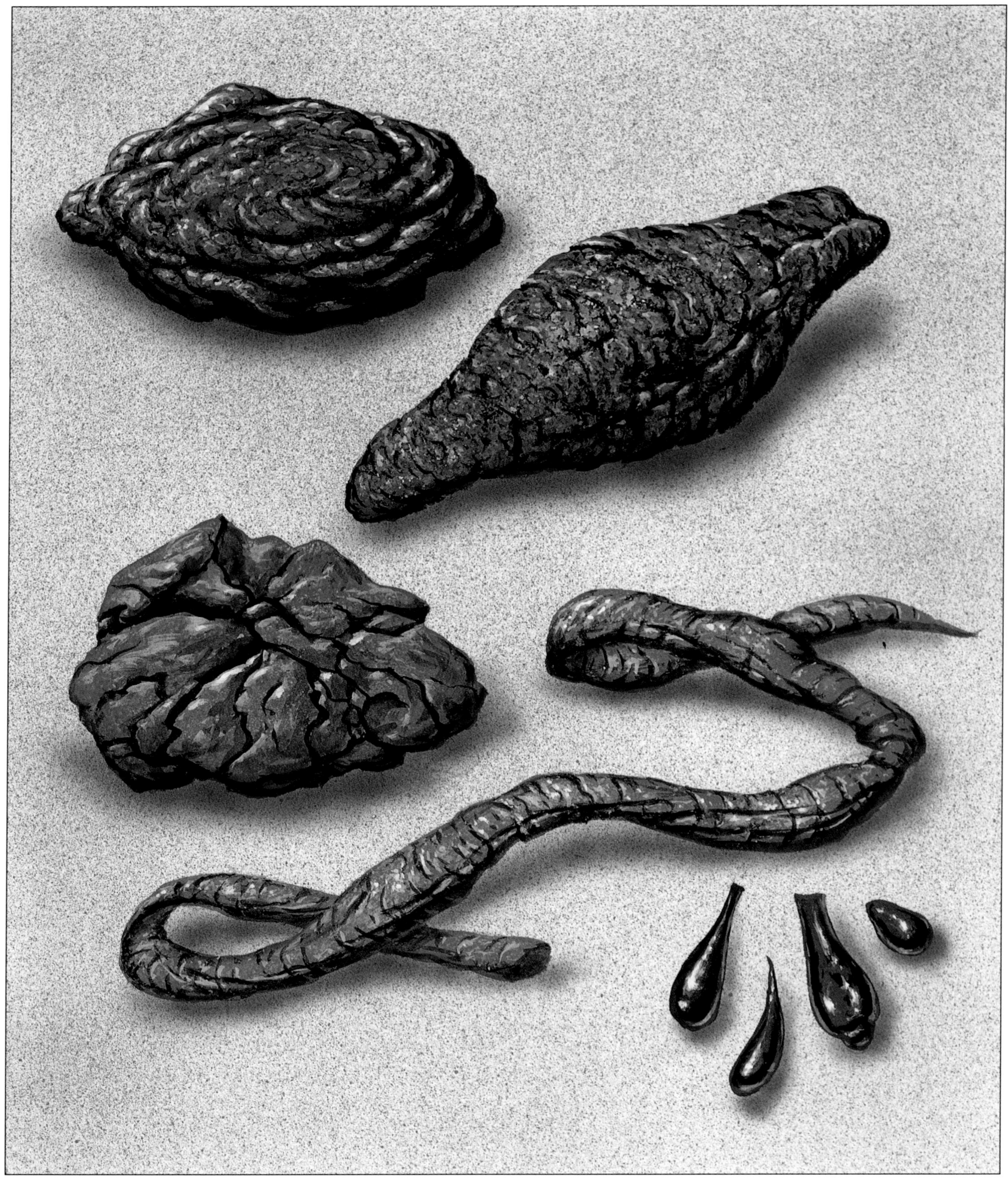

BOMBS, LAPILLI AND SCORIA

A volcanic bomb (see p. 44) is a general name for a lump of solid or partly liquid rock that is thrown out of a volcano, but to qualify for this name it must be bigger than 1¼ in (32 mm) in diameter.

There are several types of volcanic bomb. At the start of an eruption, when the volcano is 'clearing its throat', fragments of rock from the vent walls, or rocks of solidified lava which sealed the vent after the previous eruption, are ejected. These solid projectiles of older lava are called *lithic blocks* and are usually angular and visibly derived from the break-up of a larger mass of rock. In some cases, however, they may fall back into the vent and be thrown out again, or even rise and fall several times inside the vent before landing outside the crater. When this happens, these lithic bombs become smooth and rounded at the edges and may end up almost spherical or ellipsoidal, sometimes partly or totally coated in a skin of fresh lava.

When clots of fresh molten lava are thrown out, the bombs look very different. They are usually very dark, often appearing shiny when looked at closely, but rough and vesicular (filled with bubbles) and irregularly shaped. These are ordinary *scoriaceous bombs*, or simply *scoria*, a name that is used for the loose, rubbly material that piles up around a strombolian eruption. But if the lava is of low viscosity (very liquid), it remains liquid throughout its flight through the air and splashes on to the ground to form an aptly named *cowpat bomb*. However, the imaginary cows would have to be very large as their 'droppings' may reach 3–10 ft (1–3 metres) in diameter. When hundreds of cowpat bombs pile up on top of one another, the resulting heap of flattened bombs fused together while still molten is known as spatter, and cones built up of this material are known as spatter cones (see p. 44).

If the lava is less fluid, beautiful aerodynamic shapes may form as the lava stretches, twists and deforms in flight. *Ribbon bombs* form when sticky lava is stretched out in flight like dribbles of syrup; some attain 13 ft (4 metres) in length and occasionally exotic shapes, such as rings up to 10 ft (3 metres) across may form. More often, these ribbons break up and spin during flight to form *spindle bombs*, sometimes called *fusiform bombs*. In these both ends of a lump may be stretched out, or if only one end is elongated, a teardrop- or bottle-shaped bomb is created. Sometimes the two ends of a spindle bomb are bent into a boomerang shape in the headlong plummet back to earth.

All liquid bombs may develop an *aerodynamic flange* as they accelerate back to earth, formed by the rushing air dragging back the malleable surface. They may also acquire a *breadcrust surface*, where the outer skin only has solidified during flight. This thin outer skin shatters into a crazed pattern of cracks when it hits the ground, to be quickly frozen in place as the inside solidifies. *Secondary craters* will form if the bomb is heavy enough and falls from high enough. These are impact craters, excavated as the bomb hits the ground and throws out ash and scoria to form a crater.

Lapilli is the correct name for particles thrown out of a volcano which are too small to be called bombs and too large to be ashes. Measuring ⅕–1¼ in (4–32 mm) across, they are defined as volcanic projectiles, but are essentially little bombs. Aerodynamic shapes are not unusual, and sometimes it is possible to find beautiful examples of spindle bombs only ½ in (1 cm) across, complete with aerodynamic flange; strictly speaking, these should be referred to as spindle lapilli.

Very fluid lavas, such as those of Hawaii, produce two remarkable and aptly named types of volcanic projectile. *Pélé's tears* are tiny, teardrop-shaped driblets of shiny, glassy lava ejected during fire fountaining and are named after the Hawaiian goddess of volcanoes. The 'tears' usually have a long thin strand of glass trailing from them, which breaks off and gently floats to earth, sometimes being carried several miles if a wind is blowing. This curious projectile is known as *Pélé's hair*. In Hawaii these strands sometimes accumulate downwind of the eruption to form a thick mat looking remarkably like golden brown hair.

TYPES OF VOLCANIC ROCK

Volcanic rocks may be broadly divided into *lavas*, which are molten rocks that flow out of a volcano along the ground, and *pyroclastics* (sometimes called *tephra*), which are thrown through the air before reaching their final resting place. A volcano will normally erupt both lava and pyroclastic rocks during the same eruption, so both types may be formed from the same magma.

Lavas can be classified according to their chemical composition. *Basalts* are the simplest lavas, formed from the melting of the upper mantle. They are dense, usually grey-black in colour and contain about 50 per cent silica. *Andesites* are more complex, being derived not only from the melting of the upper mantle but also the lower part of the continental crust – the oceanic

Types of volcanic rock. *The colours and markings shown here are the best known, but it must be emphasized that the appearance of rocks within these groups may vary considerably.*

Vesicular basalt: *The bubbles (vesicles) in this rock are caused by expanding gas during eruption.*

Andesite: *Fine-grained, very hard rock (sometimes purplish-red) which contains small crystals of feldspar.*

Rhyolite: *The most acidic volcanic rock. Some examples, like this one, show streaks resulting from the flowing lava.*

Pumice: *A light, honeycombed rock in which the gas bubbles have expanded, thus making it able to float on water.*

Tuff: *A crumbly rock consisting of loosely consolidated fragments which may be either solid or molten when erupted.*

Ignimbrite: *A light-coloured rock consisting of many fragments, including pumice and dark glass, which are often twisted into flame shapes during eruption.*

Obsidian: *The finest (and rarest) examples of this rock resemble pure black glass.*

crust – and even sediments dragged down by subduction zones. They contain more silica (about 60 per cent), a different set of minerals and tend to be a lighter grey in colour, with small white crystals. *Rhyolite* has the highest silica content (more than 65 per cent), making it the most acidic. Typically, it is even lighter in colour than andesite. *Obsidian* is a rare type of rhyolite, and at its best may be a pure black glass.

Pyroclastic rocks are more commonly classified according to structure and mode of emplacement, rather than composition. Ash may compact to form *tuff*, a gritty rock, usually with prominent layering and often crumbly. Better known is *pumice*, usually formed from acidic magma suddenly depressurized during a violently explosive eruption. The gas bubbles expand within it to make a light, honeycombed rock that floats on water. *Ignimbrite* in its original meaning refers to the extensive deposits of large pyroclastic flows. In its best-known form, the rock itself is pale, containing many fragments. These are characteristically flattened and twisted into flame shapes, called *fiamme*, as they were still hot and plastic when they came to rest.

OVERLEAF: *Torrential storms, mudflows and ashfalls associated with big volcanic eruptions may cause more death and destruction than the eruptions themselves.*

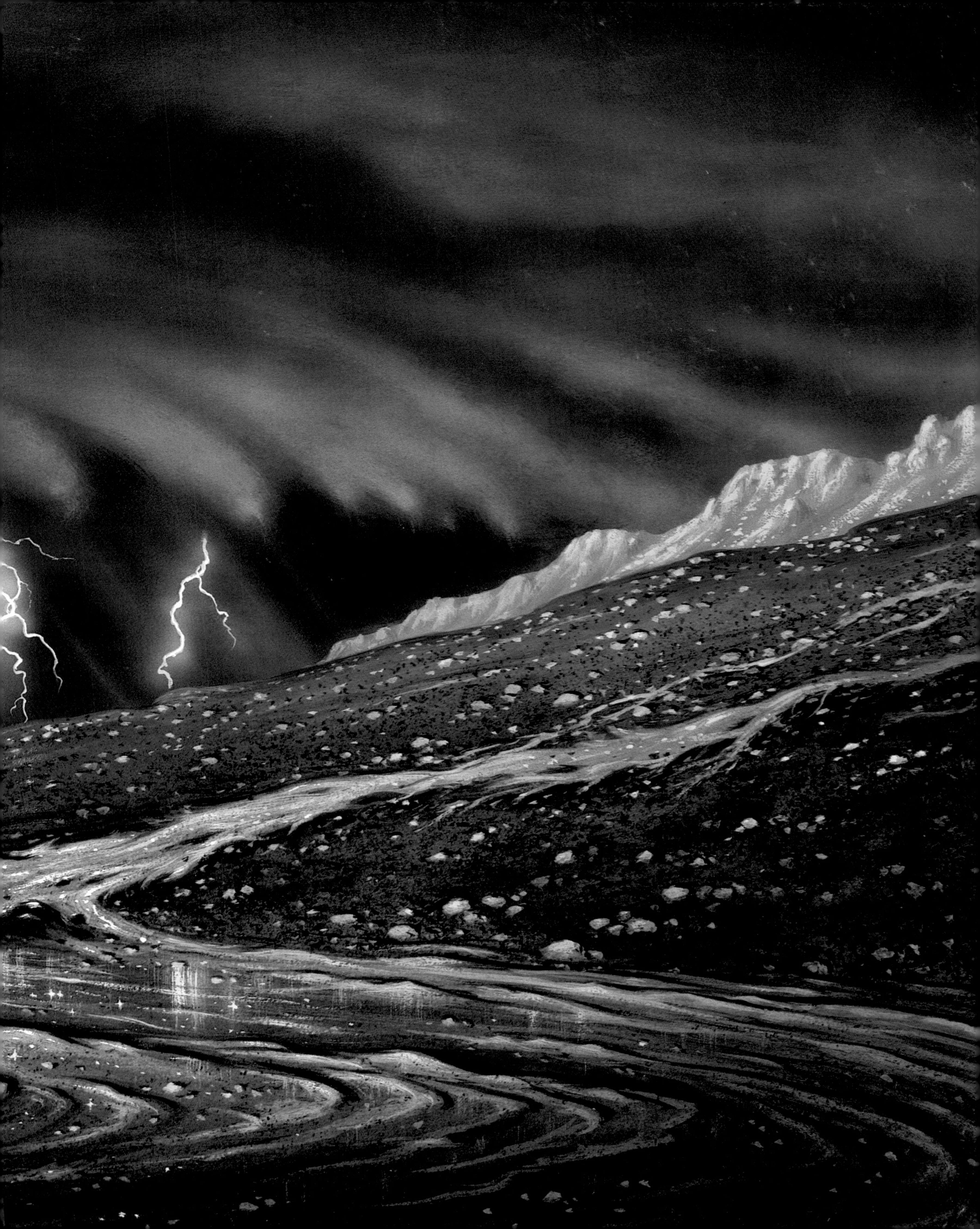

ASSOCIATED PHENOMENA

When volcanic eruptions become violent, they start to have dramatic effects on the atmosphere around them and to create their own weather. One of the first signs of such influence is the appearance of electric discharges within the eruptive cloud. The upward rush of so many tiny particles creates enormous static charges in different parts of the cloud in the same way that hailstones do as they are carried on updraughts in a thunderstorm. The resulting discharge looks identical to lightning, but the dry electric crack accompanying it sounds distinctively different from the peal and rumble of thunder.

Persistent or larger eruptions of plinian type produce much more heat and send much more material into the atmosphere. This may create enormous updraughts and therefore high winds as air rushes in to replace the rapidly rising air mass over the volcano. A secondary result may be the generation of unnaturally large thunderstorms and torrential rain downwind of the volcano. Mixed with the huge volumes of fine ash already in the air, this can produce mud rain that may be more devastating than the strictly volcanic effects of the eruption. This kind of associated weather disturbance was graphically described by the passengers aboard the *Loudon* during her passage near Krakatoa in 1883 (see p. 10).

Another result of torrential rain on volcanic slopes may be a *lahar*, an Indonesian word meaning a volcanic mudflow. However, some of the most disastrous mudflows have been caused by the sudden discharge of huge amounts of water near the top of the volcano, either by sudden drainage of a crater lake, or by the sudden melting of ice or snow near the summit.

In the largest and most explosive eruptions, so much fine ash may be ejected into the atmosphere that sunlight may be reduced over much of the Earth's surface. Widespread effects of this type were first noticed in the Laki Fissure eruption of 1783, when a 'dry fog' making the sun feeble was noticed all over Europe and North America throughout the summer. This meant that winter arrived early and was unusually severe. One hundred years later, in 1883, the eruption of Krakatoa produced a bigger ash cloud that was better defined and much better documented. This spread rapidly westwards across the Indian Ocean, reaching Ceylon the following day and travelling right round the Earth back to Krakatoa in a fortnight. In this first circuit of the Earth the dust kept close to the Equator at about the same latitude as Krakatoa, but in the following weeks, as it continued to circle the Earth, it also gradually spread north and south as well, reaching the latitude of the British Isles in November and producing spectacular sunsets, coloured moons and associated optical phenomena, as well as sky haze. Similar effects were noted after the Mount Katmai eruption of 1912 in Alaska, which produced the Valley of Ten Thousand Smokes ignimbrite, and particularly after the Mount St Helens eruption in 1980 and the El Chichón, Mexico, eruption of 1982.

These last two eruptions were interesting as they were the first to be studied with modern, ground-based and satellite-borne equipment such as lidar (see p. 151), which can detect the height as well as the intensity of layers of volcanic dust in the atmosphere. This showed dust layers as high as 14 miles (23 km) for the Mount St Helens eruption and 18 miles (30 km) for the El Chichón eruption. The latter volcano was heavily forested and had not been active in historic time. There had been much premonitory earthquake activity in the area for some weeks beforehand, but no one expected an eruption here and no volcanologist arrived until after the eruption had occurred. It began half an hour before midnight on 28 March 1982 with a series of very large explosions, and further explosive events occurred on 30 March and 4 April, when a pyroclastic flow destroyed a village 4 miles (7 km) from the volcano. Altogether about 2000 people died. Lidar measurements around the world showed that fine ash particles from this eruption were still detectable in the atmosphere nearly four years later, when the Nevado del Ruiz volcano in Colombia erupted and also sent large quantities of ash around the world which obscured the El Chichón ash. The 1991 eruption on Pinatubo in the Philippines (see p. 157) launched about twice as much material into the atmosphere as El Chichón. It will be interesting to see what effect this has on climate over the next few years.

These studies have prompted many investigations into past, large volcanic eruptions and the effects they have had on climate. Studies of climate associated with an earlier, much bigger event, the Tambora (Indonesia) eruption of 1815 – probably the largest explosive eruption in recent history – show that it was followed by an exceptionally cold and cloudy summer in 1816, with July temperatures in Britain still the coldest on record, as are the October temperatures for 1817.

The biggest drop in world surface temperatures since 1860 occurred between 1902 and 1907, when a

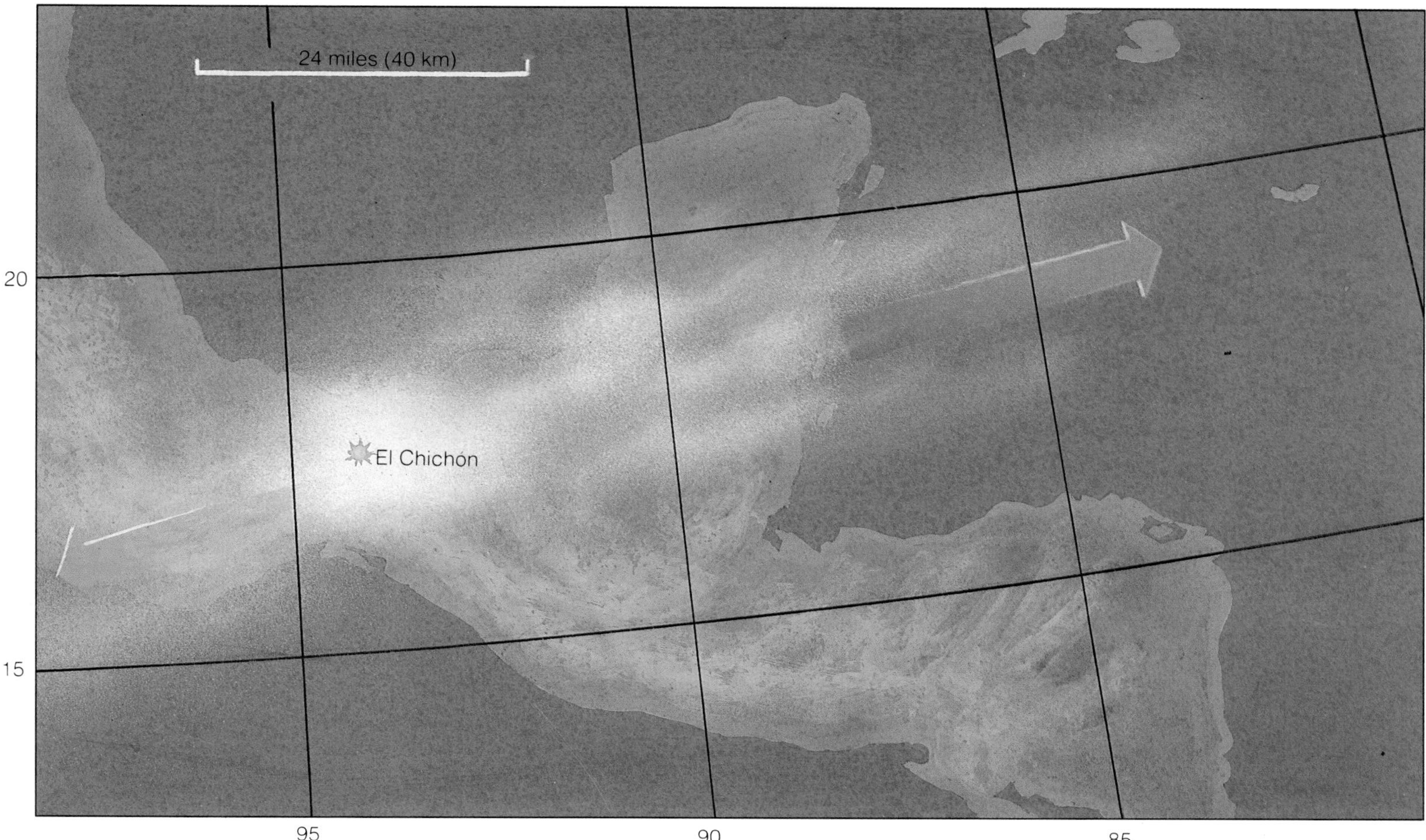

At 10.00 a.m. on 29 March 1982 the NOAA geostationary weather satellite returned images showing that a dense eruption cloud from El Chichón volcano, Mexico, was being carried both east and west by differential wind directions at different altitudes. It eventually spread around the Earth.

drop of nearly half a degree Celsius occurred. The year 1902 was when Mount Pelée, Soufrière de St Vincent and Santa Maria, Guatamala, all produced major explosive ash eruptions, that of Santa Maria being by far the biggest. In 1903 Colima volcano added to this abnormal volume of dust in the atmosphere with another huge explosive eruption. The relative sizes of some very big historic and prehistoric eruptions are given in the table (right), which provides considerable food for thought.

If eruptions like Laki and Tambora can have such a worldwide effect on climate, how much more serious would be the climatic effect of even bigger eruptions like Fish Canyon (100 times bigger than Tambora) or the many other ignimbrites almost as big that are known to have been erupted in the past?

As the lidar measurements on the El Chichón eruption show, even fine dust is unlikely to remain in the atmosphere in large quantities for more than five years, but if an increase in volcanic activity produced such huge eruptions on a regular scale, could a serious lowering of world temperatures occur and provoke an ice age? Such an idea is controversial and there is certainly no evidence that past ice ages were associated with any increase in volcanic activity. Nevertheless, it is clear that major effects on climate, even if they lasted only a few years, must have followed these huge eruptions of the past.

Eruption	*Volume cubic miles (cubic km)*	*Maximum eruption rate cubic miles (cubic km) per minute*	*Maximum ejection velocity feet (metres) per second*
Fish Canyon 28,000,000 BP*	720 (3000)	–	–
Taupo AD 186	24 (100)	3.6 (15)	1000 (300)
Santorini 1470 BC	7 (30)	0.5 (2)	1080 (330)
Tambora 1815	6 (25)	–	–
Santa Maria 1902	5 (20)	1.6 (7)	885 (270)
Krakatoa 1883	3 (12)	–	–
Mount Katmai 1912	3 (12)	–	–
Laki Fissure 1783	2.6 (11)	–	–
Vesuvius AD 79	1.4 (6)	0.2 (1)	740 (225)
Mount St Helens 1980	0.26 (1.1)	.07 (0.3)	460 (140)
El Chichón 1982	0.23 (1)	–	–

*Before present

7
UNDER THE VOLCANO

THE INTERNAL PLUMBING OF A VOLCANO

The insides of a volcano have long been a subject of curiosity and interest. Until recently, the only way of exploring inside was to find an old volcano that had been dissected by erosion so that its internal structure could be studied at first hand. There are several such volcanoes in Scotland and Wales, for example, and by studying different ones eroded to different depths it is possible to build up a general picture of the interior. In the last thirty or so years geophysical techniques have gradually been introduced which enable us to 'see' inside an active volcano and to follow what is happening there. These will be described later.

Volcanoes represent the point at which the molten magma beneath the ground reaches the Earth's surface, so the simplest structure of any volcano will involve a vertical tube or *volcanic pipe* through which the magma rises. Many volcanoes show signs of a large magma storage area near the surface called a *magma chamber*, though the word 'chamber' may be somewhat misleading, as examination of dissected volcanoes suggests that it is often a complex grid of interconnected narrow slots rather than the single rounded cavern that the name suggests. Some volcanoes show no evidence of such a storage area, however, while others show signs of two or more magma chambers at different depths. The depth of a magma chamber beneath an active volcano may be determined from earthquake studies and the way the chamber causes the surface to dome up or subside as it fills or empties with magma. Depths determined in these ways vary from 1–12 miles (2–20 km).

Beneath the magma chamber there is also one or more vertical passageways up which magma rises from the zones where it is generated by partial melting deep down. Details of the plumbing system seem to vary from volcano to volcano and have only been determined for well-studied volcanoes. The best known is probably Kilauea on Hawaii, whose subsurface structure is shown opposite. Magma rises up a more or less vertical primary conduit 3–6 miles (5–10 km) wide, which has slight twists and turns and thicker sections 6–25 miles (10–40 km) below the surface. Above a depth of about 6 miles (10 km) the conduit suddenly broadens out into magma storage areas. The main storage area for the summit is at a depth of about 1–2 miles (2–3 km), but from either side of this run two 'rift zones' east and southwest in which molten magma is also stored. Eruptions may occur either within the summit caldera, or magma may migrate along cracks and weaknesses in the rift zones to break surface there as a flank or rift-zone eruption. Magma-filled cracks formed in this way are known as dykes (see p. 85), so the rift zones between the subsurface storage areas and the surface must consist of thousands of solidified dykes accumulated over the centuries. The rift-zone storage areas are tall – about 6 miles (10 km) high – but fairly narrow, and magma accumulating in the central chamber may suddenly migrate into one of the rift zones without erupting to add to the magma already stored there.

Mount Etna has not been so intensively studied as Kilauea, but evidence from a number of sources suggests a slightly different plumbing system. There appears to be a large, flattish storage area about 12 miles (20 km) down, above which a pipe rises to the surface, but there seems to be no shallow magma chamber like that at Kilauea. Etna is also different from Kilauea in that there are four summit craters, but there is evidence that they are connected at shallow depths about ½ mile (1 km) down. The main column rising from the deep magma chamber is always full of magma, exposed to the air at the top where it can be heard degassing explosively within at least one of the summit craters. Summit eruptions occur when the magma rises up one of the summit craters and overflows, but every now and again the flanks split and dykes of magma are injected horizontally to form a flank eruption. These flank eruptions occur preferentially along two 'rift zones' running northeast and south, but unlike the Hawaiian rift zones, there is no evidence of storage of molten magma beneath them; they simply appear to be the zones of weakness along which magma usually travels from the central pipe to the flank eruption site.

Krafla volcano in Iceland has a different plumbing system again. Unlike Kilauea and Etna, Krafla is not a continuously erupting volcano; indeed, it erupts very infrequently. The series of eruptions between 1724 and 1729, known as the 'Myvatn fires', was its only recorded activity before the recent reactivation, which began in 1975 with a small eruption, and continued for the next nine years with a series of several short-lived eruptions (see p. 46). Krafla is also in a different tectonic situation, being in the centre of the Mid-Atlantic Ridge, a spreading axis, whereas Kilauea is a mid-plate volcano over a hot spot and Etna is on a plate margin between two converging continents.

At Krafla all the evidence points to a magma chamber with a diameter of about 2 miles (3 km), slightly offset from the centre of the 5-mile (8-km) diameter surface caldera, with the roof of the chamber at a depth of 2 miles (3 km). However, the central vent area marking the pipe or chimney connecting this magma chamber to the surface is not well-defined as it is at both Kilauea and Etna, and the eruptions that occurred between 1975 and 1984 all came from a series of new north–south fissures. These groups of fissures were typically 3–6 miles (5–10 km) long and extended well outside the bounding faults of the caldera.

Evidence from several sources indicates that after east–west extension of the region, magma fills the chamber from beneath, causing it to swell until the roof cracks. The magma fills these cracks and escapes to the surface to produce an eruption. Much of the magma is intruded, however, and it is clear that while the eruptive fissures are only a few miles long at the surface, beneath the ground they may extend for 25 miles (40 km). In addition, many episodes of intrusion occurred without eruption. During the 1975–84 series of eruptions, magma took three to nine months to fill the chamber, but once the roof of the chamber had split, magma took only one to seven hours to rise up the cracks and reach the surface as an eruption.

VOLCANIC INTRUSIONS

The transport of magma from deep inside the Earth to the surface takes place through conduits and storage areas that have characteristic shapes, depending upon the viscosity of the magma and the planes of weakness in the *country rock*, a general term for the rock through which magma is injected, which may be either sedimentary or volcanic. Often the magma solidifies in these underground regions without ever reaching the surface. Any magma-filled cavity created through the forcing apart of older rock is known as an *intrusion*.

The most common of the near-surface intrusions are *dykes* – vertical, magma-filled cracks which open, as described in the previous section, in response to mag-

The plumbing system of three volcanoes: Kilauea volcano, Hawaii (top), Mount Etna, Sicily (centre), and Krafla volcano, Iceland (bottom).

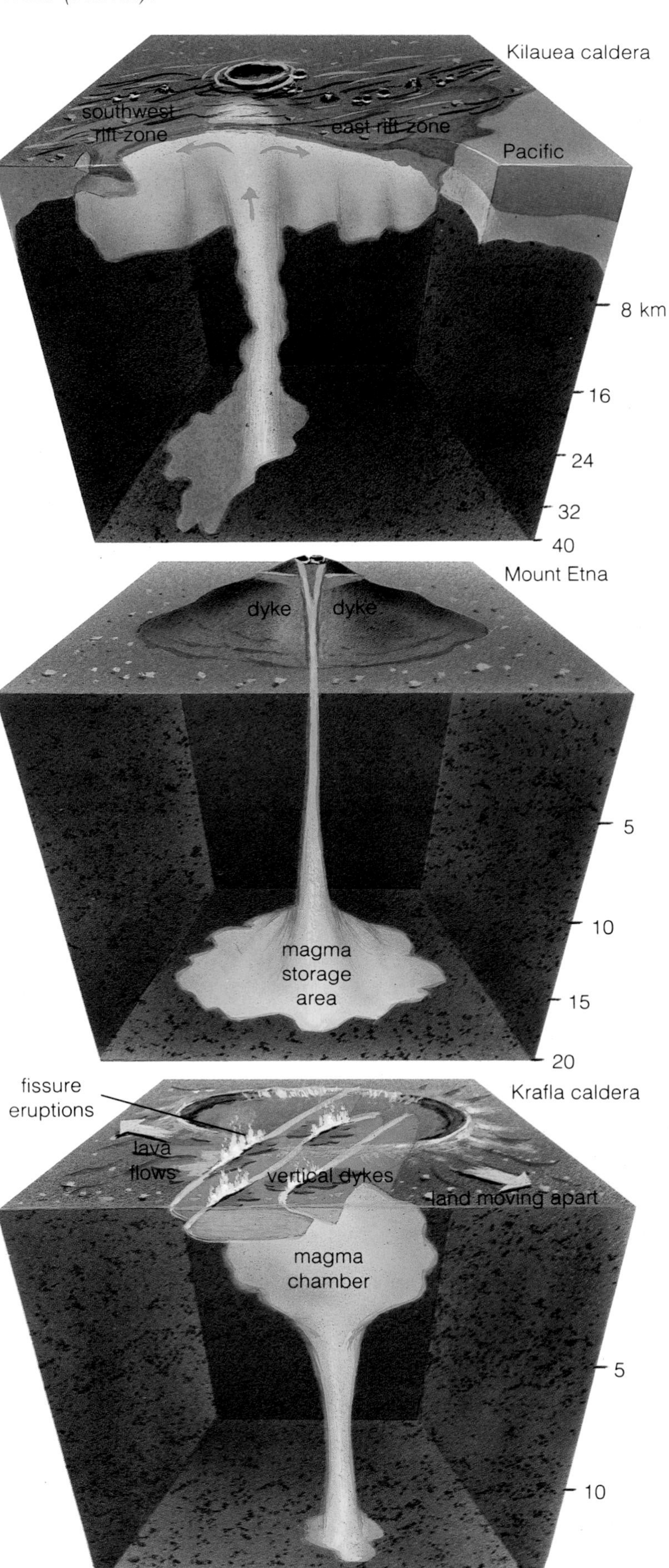

ma pressure from beneath, or as a result of the surface moving apart, allowing magma to rise. Dykes are formed by fluid magmas of comparatively low viscosity, which can fill the crack rapidly. Though most commonly a few feet thick, in extreme cases they can vary from a fraction of an inch up to a mile or so across. By definition they are more or less vertical; in practice they may incline up to 20 degrees from the vertical due to topographic or local effects changing the path of least resistance. Once the magma has solidified and the surface begins to be eroded, these dykes will stand out as long walls, or if the rock into which they have been intruded is less susceptible to erosion, as ditches. Such dykes are commonly found in many old volcanic areas of Scotland, for example, where they often occur in large *dyke swarms*, consisting of hundreds of roughly parallel dykes, marking out the position of an ancient rift zone or other line of weakness. Dykes which have been injected radially from a central magma column within a large volcano are known as *radial dykes*. Observations on active volcanoes indicate that such dykes form rapidly – from within a few hours to a few days.

As well as radial dykes, there are also concentric dykes of two types. *Ring dykes* surround a volcanic centre in a series of arcuate curves, or sometimes as a complete circle, and may be vertical or dip outward, i.e. their radius increases with depth. Ring dykes are usually thick – from 300 ft (100 metres) up to nearly 1 mile (2 km) in width – since the block of land within the ring is free to sink under gravity and allow the dyke to broaden easily. *Cone sheets*, on the other hand, dip inwards and are thus narrow – usually less than 6 ft (2 metres) thick and virtually always less than 16 ft (5 metres).

One of the finest complexes of ring dykes and cone sheets is found in the Ardnamurchan peninsula of the west coast of Scotland, where the roots of an old volcano are exposed. The three centres of different ages show that the volcano gradually evolved and the centre of activity changed position during the volcano's lifetime. The cone sheets become steeper nearer the centre of the complex and extrapolating this angle of dip beneath the surface, they converge at a point about 2 miles (3 km) down, presumably the magma chamber. Cone sheets were formed when pressure within the magma chamber was high, forcing the centre of the volcano to rise, eventually by thousands of feet, and the ring dykes were formed when the magma chamber had drained, or when the pressure was very low, allowing the centre to drop, probably as a caldera collapse at the surface.

Where magma is injected in a horizontal sheet between previous layers of rock, it is known as a *sill*. Sills 100 ft (30 metres) thick or more are found in Scotland and northern England, and near New York a sill 1000 ft (300 metres) thick follows the bank of the Hudson River. Where the magma is more viscous, a special form of sill occurs known as a *laccolith*, in which the strata overlying the intrusion are domed upwards. Sometimes more complex forms occur in which subsidiary laccoliths are stacked above each other and the outer edges of a laccolith may grade into a sill. Where magma is injected laterally into folded strata, a kind of cross between laccolith and sill can occur. Lens-shaped masses of magma called *phacoliths* are found occupying the saddles of anticlines or the keels of synclines (i.e. the hills and valleys of the folds) where the rigid rock sheets naturally gape apart in the folding process.

Deeper intrusions of magma on a larger scale are known by various names. In some regions, particularly above subduction zones beneath continents, such as the Andes in South America, huge balloons of granitic magma formed at depth may slowly make their way upwards, like oil through water, and solidify a few miles below the surface. Such a mass of magma, usually several miles wide, is generally known as a pluton (see p. 39), but a smaller, similar massive intrusion which broadens with depth is usually called a *stock*, or a *boss* if it is more or less circular in cross-section. Plutons make their way upward by *stoping*, a process in which *xenoliths*, sections of the roof of the pluton, fall into it and sink to the bottom where they become the floor. Stoping ceases in the upper parts of the crust where the pieces of roof are less dense than the magma, so they float on it and remain in place.

A batholith (see p.39) is the name given to a much larger accumulation of granite rock where several plutons have gathered over millions of years. Batholiths usually occur within the heart of mountain ranges, and may be up to 1250 miles (2000 km) long.

A magma chamber is also a form of intrusion and many of the above features are found in association with magma chambers. In particular, it is probable that stoping is also an important process in the development or upward migration of magma chambers. The chamber will find its own depth through neutral buoyancy, i.e. when the density of the rocks through which it rises is the same density as the magma itself. Some of the rock surrounding the magma chamber will inevitably become detached and incorporated into the magma, and in some cases this 'contamination' can cause important changes in composition.

The wall rocks of all intrusions will in any case be baked and altered to some degree through a process known as *contact metamorphism*, where the rock is directly in contact or very close to the magma, or through *thermal metamorphism*, where heat is the cause of the change in the rocks. This kind of metamorphism is most important for the large, long-lived sources of heat such as plutons and magma chambers. The skin of altered rock found around an intrusion is called a *metamorphic aureole*.

MAGMA

Through a process known as *differentiation*, magma may change and evolve over a period of time. If it remains stored in one chamber for any length, it will start to cool and new crystals will begin to grow. The heavier crystals within the magma will sink to the bottom of the chamber and the lighter constituents will float to the top. This ultimately means that the magma at the top of the chamber will have a different composition from that at the bottom.

An analogous process occurs with milk. When it comes out of the cow, it has a homogeneous composition, but if left to stand for a while, the lighter, fattier material within the milk separates, or differentiates, and floats to the top. This material, known as cream, acquires a slightly different composition from the rest of the milk. The longer the milk is left standing, the creamier the top. Similarly, the amount of differentiation within magma indicates how long it has been stored in the magma chamber. This differentiation

Types of volcanic intrusion.

The process of differentiation.

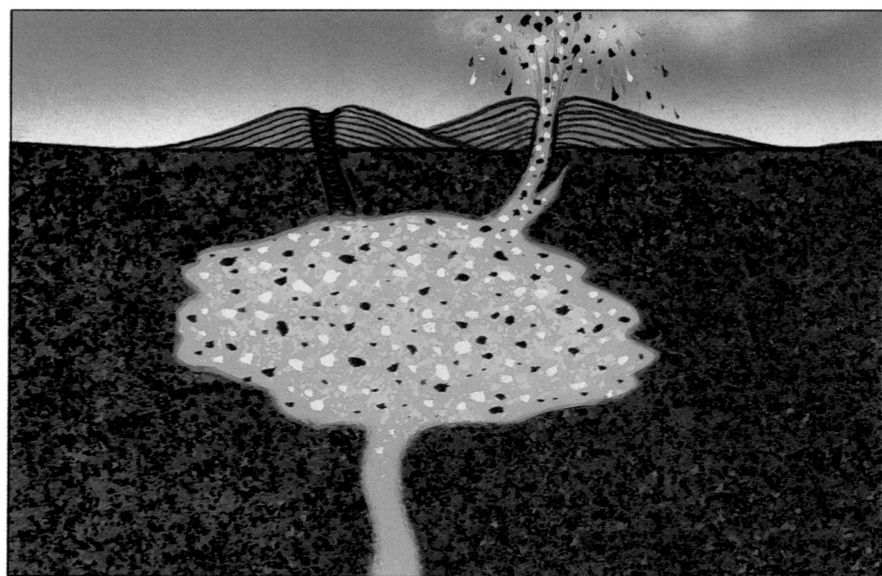

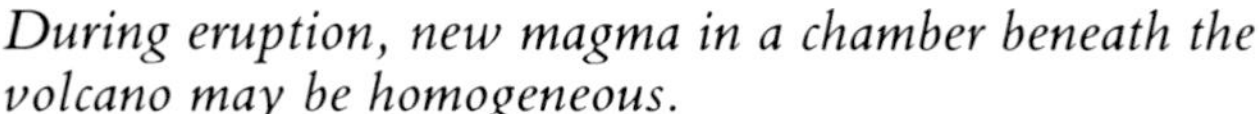

During eruption, new magma in a chamber beneath the volcano may be homogeneous.

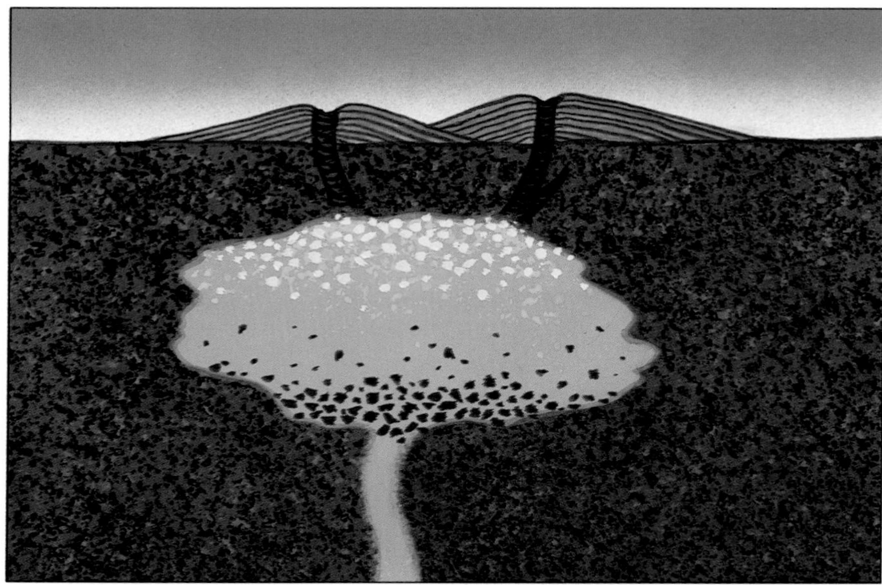

If there is a long repose period between eruptions, differentiation may occur, the heavier elements sinking to the bottom of the magma chamber, and the lighter ones rising to the top.

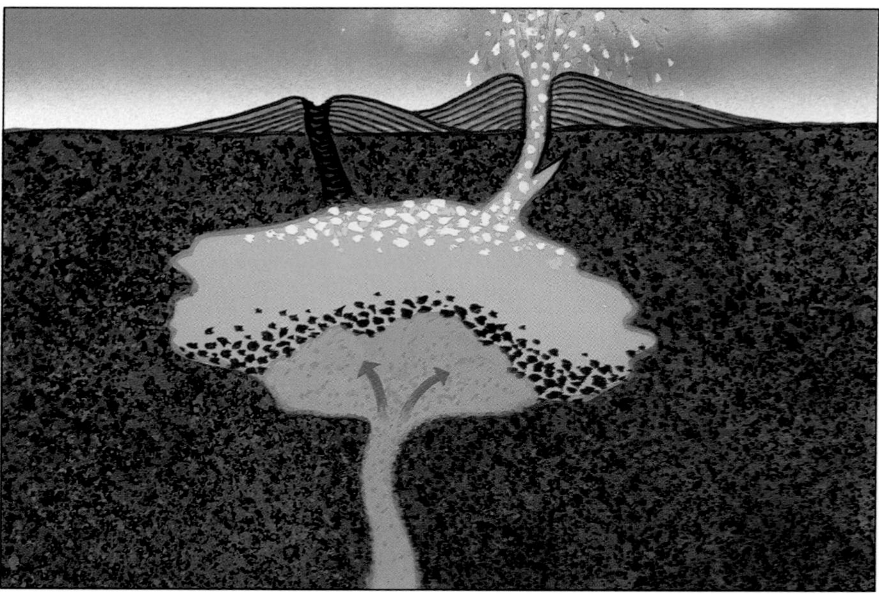

When the volcano erupts again the magma erupted first is of an 'evolved' composition, being depleted in heavier components and enriched in lighter ones. The arrival of new magma from below may start old and new batches of magma mixing within the chamber, creating a complex type of magma.

means that the magma near the top of the chamber, which will be erupted first, is rich in light minerals and depleted in heavier ones that will have fallen to the bottom.

Thanks to differentiation, the composition of lavas may change during an eruption, as first the upper and then the lower magmas are erupted. If the magma remains stored for a lengthy period (in some cases for several centuries), its composition may be significantly different at the top and bottom of the chamber. In fact, nearly all the common volcanic rocks with compositions more acidic than basalt can be produced by differentiation of basaltic magma. Although some of them *are* produced in this way, the huge volumes of acidic rocks found above subduction zones, particularly in the fold mountains of the Rockies and the Andes, make it clear that not all of them could have been formed by differentiation. Indeed, most of these magmas were derived from the melting of the lower part of the continental crust. Granite magmas are produced by parts of the crust melting in association with folding and mountain-building.

Magma is supplied to the surface at different rates in different places. The almost continuously active volcanoes, such as Etna, Kilauea and Piton de la Fournaise, which erupt lava almost every year, receive magma from depth at a higher rate than less active volcanoes such as Krafla (see p. 46), which erupts only every 200 years or so. All the volcanoes named here are basaltic with fluid magmas, so they can be compared in this way, but frequency of eruption is also related to magma viscosity. A magma of higher viscosity (less fluidity) will be able to retain the gases within it for longer and will also ascend more sluggishly so that the intervals between eruption may be longer. The amount extruded during each eruption may be correspondingly greater, however, so that over a long period the amount of magma extruded may be the same as for a more fluid magma erupted more frequently.

Although individual volcanoes are supplied with magma at a given rate over a given period, this rate may also change as time goes on. Vesuvius, for example, had not been active for centuries before the AD 79 eruption and it did not erupt again for nearly a century. There was also a long period of dormancy before the huge eruption of 1631. Yet this same volcano was almost continuously active from 1911 until 1944, since when there have again been no signs of activity. Even the more continuously active volcanoes show clear variations in magma supply. Etna has had comparatively long periods without eruptions – sixteen years at the turn of the century and fourteen years between 1928 and 1942, yet since 1950 it has been erupting lava at a rate more than four times greater than for the previous century, and this rate is still increasing. There is also evidence of *magma pulses* – sudden, short-lived increases in magma supply.

The reasons for these changes are speculative and may result from several causes, ranging from changes at great depth where the magma is generated, to changes affecting the shallow magma chamber. At any depth between these two, new storage areas may open up, allowing magma to migrate sideways to fill them and cause a temporary halt in supply, or regional tectonic movements may close off a source of magma for a time.

Volcanoes which erupt very infrequently have some of the most interesting and least understood magma supply systems. Despite the fact that they are dormant for most of the time, some of them may show curious signs of activity. A particularly worrying case is the Phlegrean Fields at Pozzuoli, near Naples in Italy. This area lies at the centre of a large caldera, and there are several old centres of volcanic activity, some of which show signs of huge and violent prehistoric eruptions. The most recent activity was in 1536, when a large new cinder cone appeared within a few days in a brief eruption.

In 1970 the ground suddenly began rising, and in a year had risen by 3 ft (1 metre) in places. The local authorities were worried and families were evacuated from some areas of poor housing which were showing signs of becoming unsafe. However, the ground ceased to rise in 1971 and life returned to normal until 1982, when, over a two-year period, the ground rose again, this time by an alarming 6 ft (2 metres). However, as before, the movement ceased and nothing else happened. It is likely that upward and downward movements of this type have been going on at least since Roman times, for the pillars of a Roman temple built on the shoreline near Pozzuoli are now under water, showing that downward movements have predominated.

Despite the fact that eruptions occur in the region only every thousand years or so on average, it is clear that even when there have been no eruptions for centuries, magma is moving around or changing in some way within the magma chamber, which earthquake data and other evidence shows to be at a depth of about 1 mile (2 km) beneath the surface.

8
ERUPTION MECHANISM

WHY ERUPTIONS OCCUR

The reasons why an eruption occurs at a particular time in a particular place have long been a source of fascination. They can be broadly summarized under two headings: *magma pressure* from below and *depressurization* (decrease in pressure) at the surface. Pressure from below is perhaps the most obvious. A buoyant magma constantly being produced deep down must eventually build up enough pressure to break through to the surface and erupt. Depressurization can be just as effective, however, for as soon as pressure on a magma chamber is relieved, gas bubbles will start to form within the magma, causing it to expand and rise upwards like uncorked champagne. Depressurization can occur by regional movements pulling apart the surface, as happens at mid-ocean ridges, where convection in the mantle is dragging the crust apart.

Eruptions caused by magma pressure are best demonstrated by the eruptions of very active volcanoes such as Kilauea. Magma steadily fills the magma chamber from below, causing the surface of the volcano to dome up over a period of months in response to the inflation of the magma chamber. When the fluid pressure within the chamber reaches a point at which it can no longer be contained by the strength of the rocks surrounding it, the chamber 'bursts' as the rocks fracture. If the roof of the chamber fractures, an eruption occurs, otherwise the walls of the chamber may fracture, causing magma to be injected laterally as an intrusion. In either case the magma chamber immediately deflates, but as soon as the eruption or the intrusion has finished, the magma chamber immediately starts to inflate again until the next eruption or intrusion occurs.

The actual position of an eruption, i.e. the place where the magma breaks the surface, will depend upon the stress regime within the volcano. Most eruptions of large, persistently active volcanoes occur at the

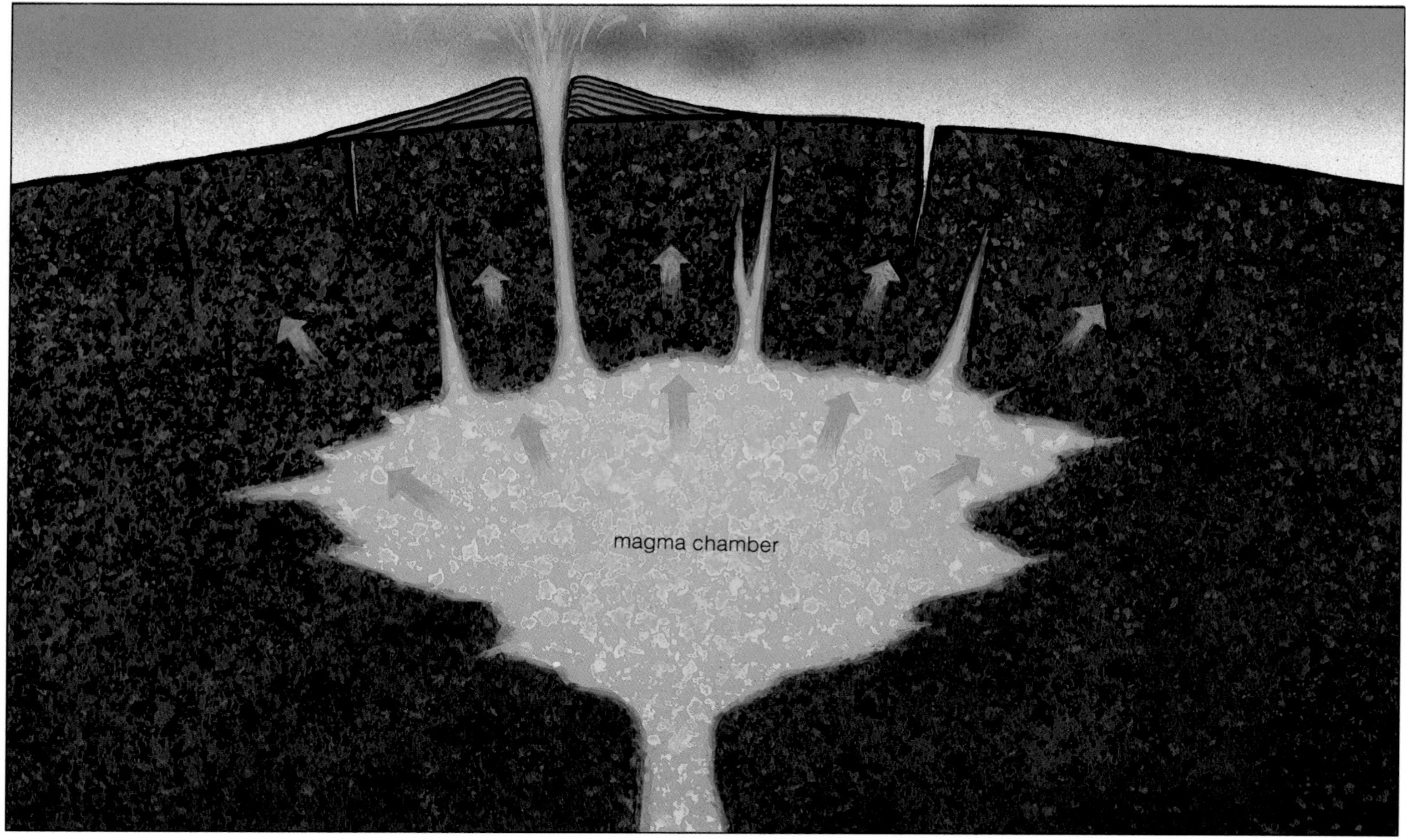

Eruptions of a volcano may be started by magma pressure, which causes the ground to dome up slightly. Eventually the rocks fracture and the magma rises through the cracks to the surface.

summit simply because magma and gas have eroded a well-defined conduit which is usually the path of least resistance for the ascending magma. However, every so often stresses or weaknesses will build up which make it easier for the magma to fracture the flanks of the volcano and create a new vent down one of the sides. Such stresses are often dominated by gravitational stress, caused by the volcano deforming under its own weight in response to its shape. The top of a ridge is a common place for an eruption to occur, as the weight of the ridge will tend to squeeze the two sides outwards, making the ridge split up the centre and permitting the magma to escape.

The actual triggering of an eruption at a particular time may be due to external causes, and in some cases there is evidence of unrelated earthquakes triggering eruptions. Colima volcano in Mexico erupted violently shortly after the great earthquake of 1806, as did Etna after the earthquake which destroyed Messina 50 miles (80 km) to the north in 1908; Puyehu volcano in Chile also erupted two days after the earthquake near Cañete in 1960. However, these volcanoes must already have been close to eruption as Colima, for example, showed no similar outburst after the 1985 earthquake. In the case of the 1908 Etna eruption, it is clear that the earthquake split the sides of the volcano, allowing the magma, which was already at a high level in the central pipe, to drain out downslope in a brief eruption lasting a few hours.

Many eruptions appear to be triggered by a magma pulse – a sudden, short-lived increase in magma supply. It has also been suggested that some eruptions may be triggered by *magma mixing* – a process by which two magmas, evolved separately and so of different composition, gas content and temperature, mix together in the same magma chamber. If the magma within a storage area is acidic, for example, the arrival of a more basic magma with a higher melting temperature from below may cause superheating in the lower part, provoking convective upward movement within the chamber and the formation of gas bubbles, which will increase the pressure. As soon as it breaks through to the surface, the sudden drop in pressure will cause an explosive eruption. Even if the two magmas are of similar composition, the simple addition of a new volume of magma to the chamber may cause the roof to fracture, provoking depressurization and a consequent uprush of magma.

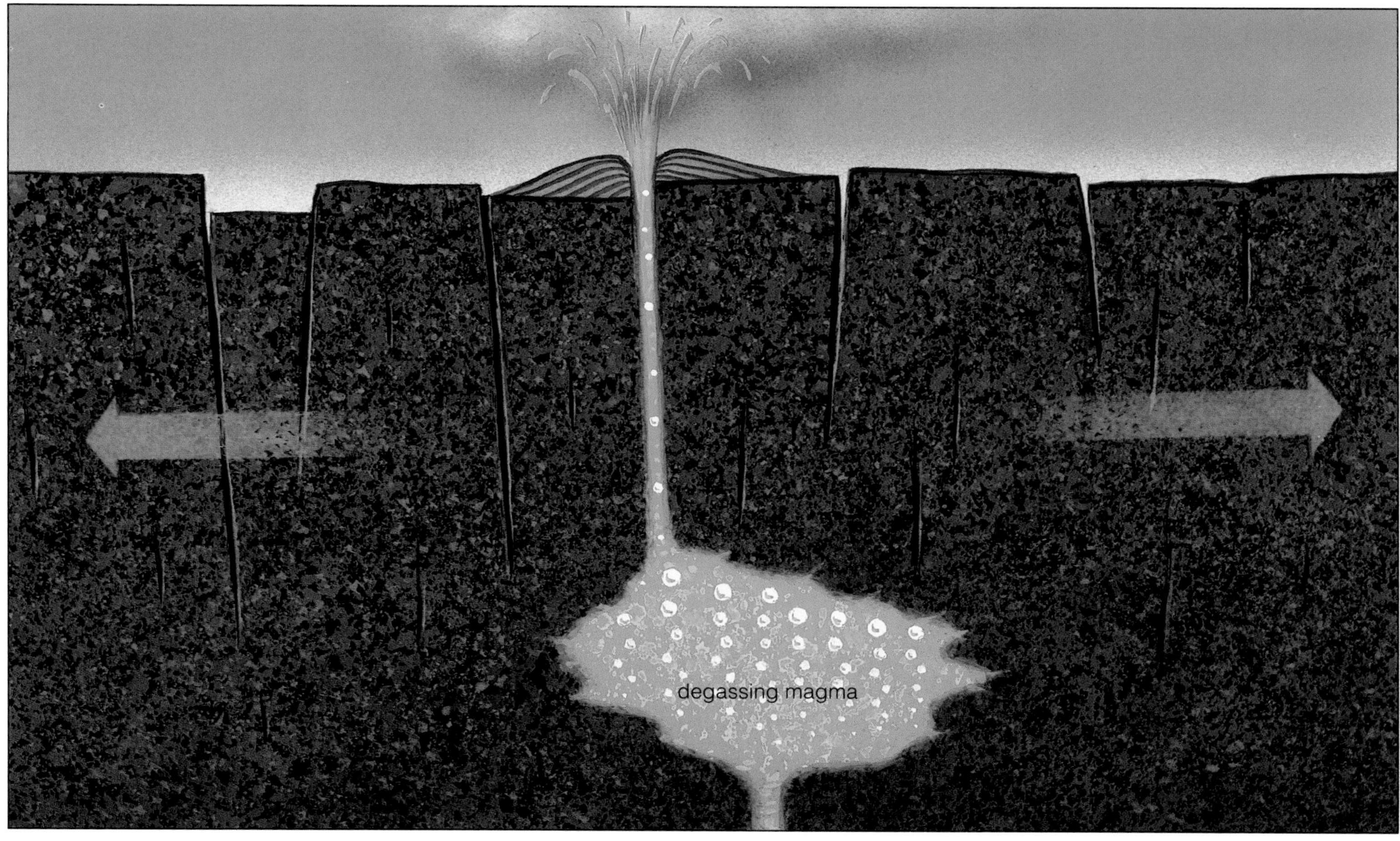

Eruptions caused by depressurization can happen when land either side of the volcano moves apart. This opens up cracks connecting the magma chamber to the surface and relieves the pressure on the magma. The magmatic gases fill the magma with rising gas bubbles, greatly increasing its volume, and it rushes up the cracks to erupt at the surface as a result.

Sections through Mount Etna before and during the 1971 eruption.

(a) *March 1971, before the eruption.*

(b) *6 April 1971.*

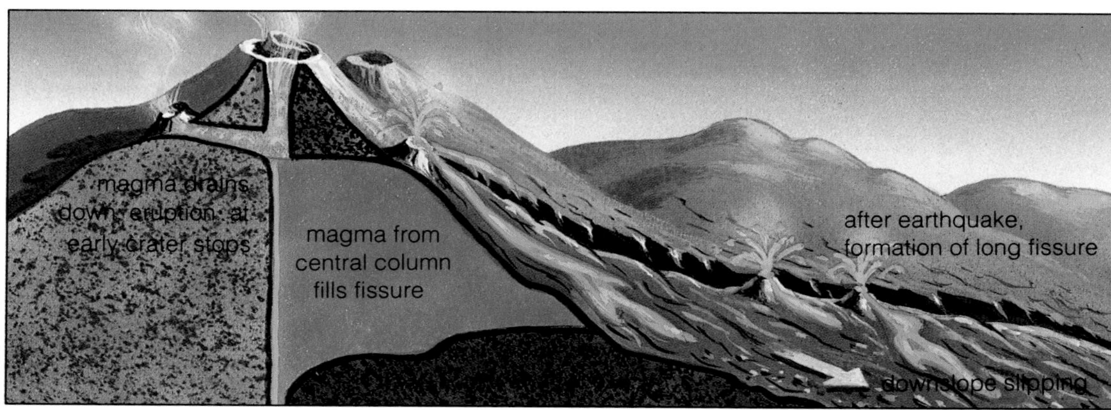

(c) *10 May 1971.*

(d) *17 May 1971.*

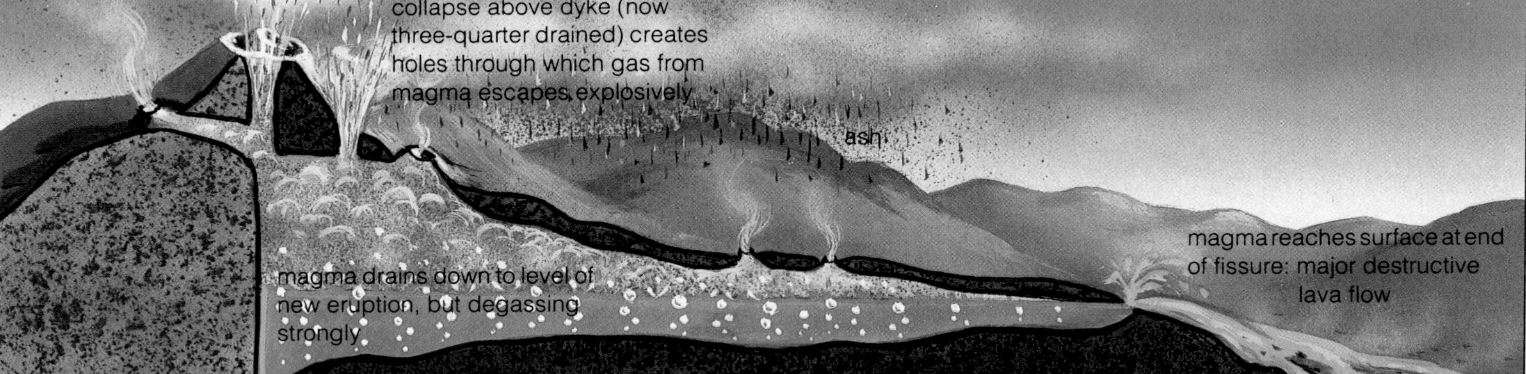

THE COURSE OF AN ERUPTION

To illustrate the workings of a highly active volcano and the chain of events that may occur during an eruption it is best to examine a typical eruption such as that of Mount Etna in 1971 (see pp 18–19), and to look at what is going on inside the volcano at each stage.

Before the eruption began Mount Etna had already been in persistent, quiet eruption at the summit on and off for sixteen years. We know, therefore, that the magma level had been high for a long time, filling the central pipe from the magma storage area 12 miles (20 km) down right up to the top of the volcano, where it frequently overflowed (a).

In early April 1971 there was a sudden increase in magma supply and the conduits which were already open were not sufficient to relieve the build-up of pressure. On 5 April the south flanks split open high up and two new dykes were formed, carrying magma from the central pipe to create two new craters at the foot of the central cone. This marked the start of the eruption. The magma immediately began degassing and the bursting bubbles at the surface caused strombolian activity that rapidly built up two new spatter cones. As soon as these new craters had opened, the magma within the volcano drained down to their level. This drop in magma level was accompanied by some collapse of the inner walls of the summit craters, causing thick clouds of dust to be emitted (b).

On 21 April a magnitude 5 earthquake occurred nearly 12 miles (20 km) away, down at the eastern foot of Etna, apparently unrelated to the eruption. However, it had a clear influence on the course of the eruption, for the disturbance caused cracks to open the following day, which were used by magma to form a new dyke to the west of the others, forming another spatter cone. Then, on 4 May, other fractures to the east, also probably opened during the earthquake, began filling with magma. First a new vent opened high up near the others, then, on 7 May, a major series of fractures began propagating down the eastern side, which filled with magma the following day to form three groups of small hornitos further downslope. On 11 May this fracture system reached its longest extent of more than 3 miles (5 km) and new vents opened at its lowest end, emitting fast-flowing lavas. As the dyke feeding these vents filled with magma, so the magma level dropped in the vents near the summit and they ceased to be active on 7 May (c).

As magma was escaping out of the lowest vent, 1 mile (1.4 km) lower in altitude than the summit, the weight of the magma above was at first considerable, forcing out the lavas at a high rate and causing them to flow faster and further. But as it drained away, so the magma level within the entire volcano continued to drop like the water in a lavatory cistern which has been flushed, and one by one the lavas from the hornitos further up the fissure stopped, all activity in them ceasing by 17 May. This withdrawal of magma from the top part of the dyke also caused a collapse pit to form near the summit, but since magma still filled the lower part of the dyke, it degassed vigorously through this upper collapse pit, causing noisy explosions and thick clouds of ash (d). In the end, the dyke became completely drained of magma and the eruption finished on 12 June.

This eruption illustrates the vagaries and inherent unpredictability of a volcano. Had the earthquake of 21 April not occurred, the eruption would probably have remained as a summit eruption, leaving a field of lava on the upper southern flanks of the volcano. Instead, a total of seven further craters or vents opened up, and being much lower down the mountain they were able to drain all the magma within the volcano above their level. This produced a higher volume eruption much nearer to inhabited areas, which eventually destroyed nearly 1 square mile (3 square km) of cultivated land.

After the eruption, remaining magma within the newly-formed dykes rapidly solidified, sealing these 'leaks' in the volcano. There continued to be short-lived increases in magma supply from deep down beneath the volcano, but these merely caused magma to froth up to the summit craters, where outbursts of strombolian activity occurred in the following months and years. The draining of Etna to such a low level meant that no lava flows came out of the volcano for another three years.

THE LIFE HISTORY OF A VOLCANO

There is a tendency to characterize volcanoes as being of certain types. Kilauea is a quiet volcano, producing a great deal of lava but very few explosions, whereas Vesuvius is a violent volcano, periodically producing the most enormous explosive eruptions. When we look at the whole history of a volcano by examining its geology, however, it is clear that its long-established character may change, sometimes permanently, so that a quietly effusive volcano may suddenly change to an extremely explosive one.

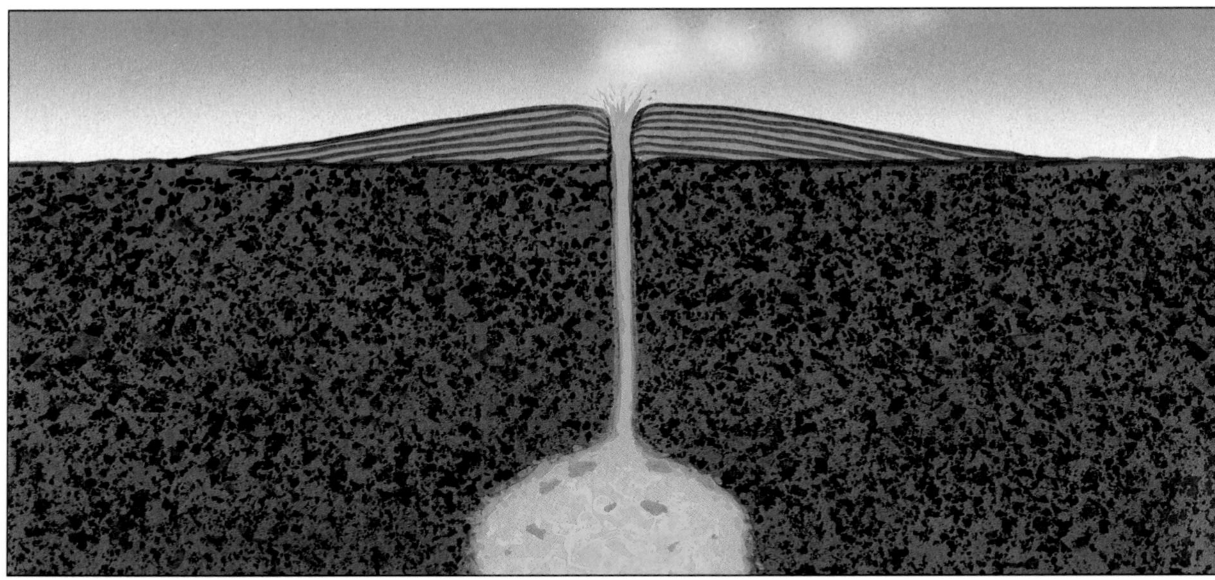

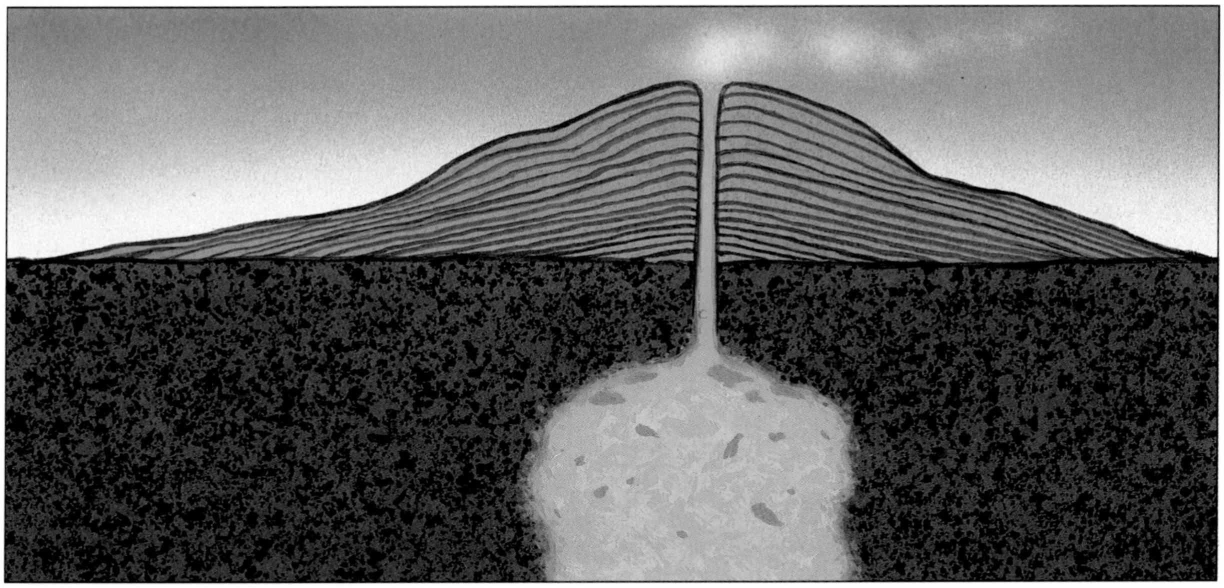

Changes in volcano type may be sudden and dramatic, even after thousands of years of quiet, 'well-behaved' eruptions.

(a) *Quiet effusion of lavas from infrequent eruptions may continue for hundreds of thousands of years.*

(b) *The development of a tall, steep volcano and a shallow magma chamber may cause the volcano to become structurally unstable.*

(c) *The result is that the top of the volcano may collapse into the magma chamber, or the side slide off in a catastrophic debris avalanche. Either event will be accompanied by instantaneous depressurization of a vast quantity of magma, and a resulting sudden and very violent eruption.*

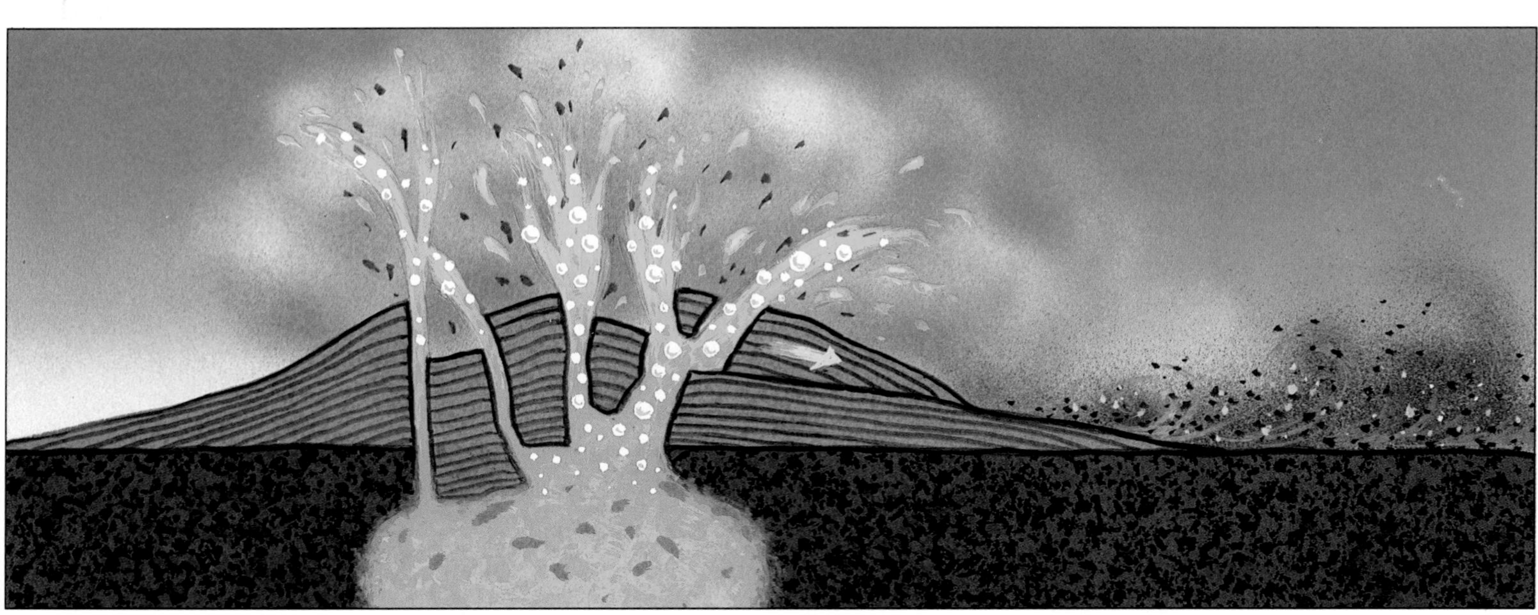

Temporary changes of this type are relatively common. Even the mild and reliable volcano of Kilauea has gone through a brief explosive period at least twice in the last 200 years. The sudden steam explosions of May 1924 were described earlier (see p. 63), and a similar outburst in 1790 was about 1000 times bigger, killing about eighty Hawaiian warriors and leaving a carpet of ash 30 ft (10 metres) thick around the crater.

More permanent changes in the character of a volcano are well illustrated in the life history of some Mexican volcanoes such as Popocatepetl, Colima and Pico de Orizaba. In these volcanoes activity begins with the quiet effusion of andesitic lava over a long period, amounting to several hundred thousand years or even more than a million years. The lava flows emitted during this period are very thick – up to 130 ft (40 metres) – with long periods of dormancy between periods of lava emission. Eventually huge volcanoes are built up, 12–20 miles (20–30 km) wide at the base and several hundred cubic miles in volume.

During all this early period there is no sign of explosive activity and these volcanoes must have resembled those on Hawaii in shape, though not in composition. The unchanging nature of the lavas suggests that they were fed from a magma chamber of medium depth in the crust, which itself was being refilled from below. Although differentiation is always taking place within this chamber, there is a continued supply of more basic magma from below. The periodical eruptions empty only a small proportion of the chamber, so more acidic magmas are never erupted.

Suddenly, there is a dramatic change. A huge caldera collapse several miles wide occurs at the summit, accompanied by cataclysmic explosive activity on a massive scale and a change in composition to much more acidic products. There is emission of pumice and large pyroclastic flows accompanied by blast and base surge which flattens and buries forests over a huge area. In some volcanoes, such as Colima, this event takes the form of sector collapse, like Mount St Helens. This cataclysm marks a transformation in the behaviour of the volcano. Activity becomes almost solely explosive for a time, and at Colima traces of 250 pyroclastic flows, pumice and ash eruptions have been found following this initial event.

The causes of this sudden schizophrenic behaviour are the development of a shallow magma chamber at the end of the first long, quiescent stage. The chamber becomes overcharged with gas and the accompanying pressure increase causes swelling, then cracking and eventual wholesale collapse of the roof to form a caldera; alternatively, the top slides off in a sector collapse. This allows most of the chamber to empty in a highly explosive manner.

There are also possible structural reasons for the change. A volcano which has been pouring out lava for hundreds of thousands of years is clearly going to be very big, and the continued piling up of thick lava flows inevitably means that it will become very high. As the viscosity of the lavas means that they can only flow for a certain distance before solidifying, the volcano cannot extend too far laterally, with the result that it becomes steeper and steeper. Eventually it becomes an unstable structure, and if it is built upon weak layers, such as clays, the whole volcano may start to spread outwards from the centre. This may open spaces at the heart of the volcano and aid the development of the shallow magma chamber.

Most importantly, when the edifice becomes too steep, the slopes are likely to fail at any time, and huge sections may peel off and slide downwards. If the summit is included in such a slide, the magma chamber may become exposed, resulting in a sector collapse and pyroclastic eruption like that at Mount St Helens volcano. Alternatively, the simple weight of the steep, tall summit overlying a shallow magma chamber may mean that it eventually sinks into the magma chamber to form a caldera, releasing rapidly depressurized magma as pyroclastic flows round the ring fractures.

Activity after this traumatic change may become mixed, with periods of lava emission for a few thousand years followed by shorter periods (1000–2000 years) of mixed cyclic activity, explosive then effusive. In Popocatepetl and Colima volcanoes both caldera collapse and sector collapse have occurred a number of times and the blast and debris flows from these events have devastated the landscape for distances approaching 60 miles (100 km). These cycles of activity seem to be related to successive periods of refilling and emptying of the near-surface magma reservoir.

These Mexican volcanoes all show sudden changes in behaviour after millenia of stability. Although not all volcanoes undergo these dramatic changes, most show clear signs of a gradually changing style of eruption on time-scales of a few years to a few thousand years, so any prediction of future activity must take into account the possibility of such changes in behaviour.

9
FAMOUS HISTORIC ERUPTIONS

LEGENDARY ERUPTIONS

The earliest accounts of volcanic eruptions, which date from more than 6000 years ago, are potentially useful in that they could extend the known record of eruptions of a particular volcano. Unfortunately, such early accounts tend to become highly coloured and altered over the centuries, so they come down to us as legends rather than factual accounts and in most cases we can only guess at their real meaning. Most volcanic areas have their mythical characters and abound with stories of fire gods, devils under the Earth, battles and falling rocks, all of which could be fanciful descriptions of one eruption or other.

One of the oldest of such legends is also one of the easiest to interpret. The Indians of Oregon have a story about a battle between the fire devil who lived on Mount Mazama and the good god of snow who lived on Mount Shasta nearby. The god of snow eventually won, but the top of Mount Mazama was destroyed in the process. Crater Lake, Oregon, now lies at the top of Mount Mazama and since this 6-mile (10-km) wide, lake-filled caldera is now known to have formed by collapse of the summit during a major ignimbrite-forming eruption around 4860 BC, it is highly likely that the Indian legend refers to this event.

Other ancient legends are not so clear. Hephaestus, the Greek god of fire, later became Vulcan, the Roman god of metal-workers, who had his forge under Mount Etna (or Vulcano according to some), and in Homer's *Odyssey* the giant Polyphemus's cave was also under Etna. As Odysseus and his men escaped from Polyphemus, he threw rocks at them, which might be a reference to some early eruption of Etna. The mention of Vulcan's forge under Etna suggests that then, as now, strombolian activity, which from a distance resembles the shower of sparks from red hot metal being struck with a hammer, was relatively common at Mount Etna, but this is far from certain.

One of the most fascinating stories of the ancient world was the Greek legend of Atlantis and its connection with the Minoan civilization which flourished at Knossos on Crete. The Greeks, who succeeded the Minoans, believed that the stories of Knossos, its King Minos and the Minotaur, were simply legends, but archaeological excavations this century have shown that much of it was based on fact. They have uncovered a remarkably advanced civilization with such modern conveniences as bathrooms, running water in copper pipes and other luxuries unknown elsewhere in the ancient world.

Santorini volcano in the Aegean Sea as it might have looked before the eruption of 1470 BC.

Santorini today.

OVERLEAF: The mythical city of Atlantis. This may be connected with the eruption of Santorini volcano in 1470 BC, and the disappearance of the Minoan civilization at about the same time.

Knossos is also the source of the legend of Daedalus and Icarus, so it is even possible that the Minoans experimented with hang gliding! They held gymnastic displays, great festivals, shows and bullfights, and their paintings, sculptures, ornaments, crockery and other utensils would not look out of place in homes today. The people had a system of writing and traded actively across the Mediterranean, particularly with Egypt, which was then also a flourishing civilization under the Pharaohs. The self-assured, peaceful, enterprising and comfortable Minoan way of life lasted for 1500 years – longer by far than the Greek Empire which followed it, the Roman Empire, or any of the subsequent European empires – yet it all came to an abrupt end around 1400 BC and no contemporary accounts survive to suggest what happened.

For many years it was assumed that Knossos had been destroyed by the Greeks, who at that time were barbaric pirates yet to develop their later cultured, scientific and philosophic reputation. But there are signs in the excavations of a very destructive earthquake and a fire. More recently, the sudden disappearance of Knossos and the Minoan civilization has been connected with the legend of Atlantis. This was first described by Plato around 400 BC, and later by Pliny the Elder (AD 23–79), though the original story had been told to the Greek traveller Solon in 590 BC by Egyptian priests.

According to the story, 9000 years before the birth of Solon there flourished the powerful kingdom of Atlantis, which consisted of nine ring-shaped islands, one inside the other, separated from each other by circular channels of water. The city on the main central island was constructed from red and black stone quarried locally and the roofs were made of copper. The island itself was rich beyond all imagination, with a racecourse around the edge and two magnificent temples embellished with gold, silver, copper and ivory. Near the temples were warm baths fed by natural hot springs.

The people of Atlantis were great seafarers, sailing all over the Atlantic Ocean, and their islands reflected their way of life. Bridges were built from one island to another and canals were dug through the rings of land so that their ships could use the enclosed channels of water as protected harbours. Sadly, Atlantis and its people were lost when, after a series of terrible earthquakes and floods, the islands were swallowed up by the sea and sank beneath the Atlantic Ocean.

This story is particularly interesting because it describes a way of life that is so similar to the Minoans': the use of copper in building, the spring-fed baths, the seafaring, the trading economy and the racecourse. The fact that the original source of the story was Egyptian priests also reinforces the connection as the Minoans and the Egyptians were trading partners for several hundred years. At the same time, the ring-shaped islands, the red and black stone, the hot springs, the earthquakes and the ultimate disappearance under the sea all suggest that the islands were volcanic – perhaps the rings of a volcanic caldera which suffered subsidence.

For centures people have wondered about the possible location of Atlantis, and so far the most likely candidate seems to be the island of Santorini (also known as Thera), which lies 60 miles (100 km) north of Knossos. Santorini suffered a gigantic eruption in 1470 BC in which a 30-square mile (80-square km) caldera was formed by collapse, an ignimbrite was released and thick ash fell for hundreds of miles. The eruption must have been similar to, but much greater than, the 1883 eruption of Krakatoa (see pp 9–11).

Such a huge eruption must have produced tsunamis that could have hit Knossos, which lies on the coast directly facing Santorini, but there is no evidence of this. It is also possible that some of the blast effects and heat from the ignimbrites would have travelled this far and added to the death and destruction. As for Atlantis, the remains of a city, probably with a population of about 30,000 people, has now been discovered on Santorini, so it is quite possible that an Aegean city-state also flourished here, as at Knossos and other places in Greece and Asia Minor, that gave rise to the legend. Having established a possible link, it is essential to allow for some elaboration in the passing down of the legend; for example, one or possibly two rings of land surrounding the central island would not be an unusual form for a pair of nested calderas,but nine rings is a bit far-fetched. Also the date and place are, perhaps not surprisingly, a long way out, but the other details seem remarkably close to the probable.

VESUVIUS, AD 79

This eruption is famous not only because it destroyed the prosperous cities of Pompeii and Herculaneum, but also because it was the first eruption for which we have a detailed, first-hand account of what happened.

Pliny the Elder, who had compiled a natural history which contained much information (and misinforma-

HARDY

The forum of Pompeii as it may have looked at the height of the Vesuvius eruption of AD *79. Ash already buries many bodies.*

tion) on volcanoes, and by curious coincidence was a source of the Atlantis legend, was killed in the AD 79 eruption of Vesuvius. His friend Tacitus, a historian, wanted to know more about the circumstances in which he met his death, so he wrote to Pliny's nephew, Pliny the Younger, requesting information. What he received back was an account so vivid and full of detail that it strikes us today as a remarkably fresh and human document.

In AD 79 Pliny the Younger was eighteen years old and he and his mother were staying with his uncle, Pliny the Elder, at Misenum, on the other side of the Bay of Naples from Vesuvius. Although destructive earthquakes had been occurring in the region for sixteen years, no one associated them with Vesuvius, which was then unknown as an active volcano and had not been in eruption for several hundred years. It was therefore a complete surprise when, on 24 August at about 2 p.m., an extraordinarily big and peculiar cloud appeared on the other side of the bay. Pliny the Elder was extremely interested by the strange sight and climbed a hill to get a better view.

The cloud, which was growing taller all the time, had a flat head, which Pliny described as being shaped like a pine tree with many branches, though he clearly meant the Mediterranean pine, which has a wider top than a Christmas spruce.

Determined to investigate more closely, Pliny the Elder ordered a fast boat to be prepared and asked his nephew if he would like to accompany him. Rather stodgily, the boy declined, saying that he would prefer to get on with his studies. However, before the boat could leave, an urgent message for help came from the other side of the bay, a prosperous area with numerous country villas. As head of the Roman fleet at Misenum, Pliny the Elder responded immediately and ordered all his warships to sail across the bay on a rescue mission. During the voyage he took notes on the activity, recording that as they came within 6 miles (10 km) of Vesuvius, the falling ashes became hotter and fell more thickly, and were followed by a hail of pumice and stones.

The thick pumice floating on the water made it impossible to land and the crew advised Pliny to turn back, but in defiant Roman manner he refused to be beaten and decided to sail around the coast to the villa of Pomponianus at Stabiae, some 10 miles (15 km) from the volcano. Once there, he seemed mainly concerned to calm everyone's fears rather than to organize evacuation, though this would have been difficult as the wind was blowing strongly towards the volcano and the villa was accessible only by water. In a typically Roman gesture, he ordered a bath to be prepared for him to show how unconcerned he was.

A few hours later it was clear that things were getting worse as fires could be seen burning in several areas. None the less, Pliny the Elder went to bed and slept soundly, even though the yard in front of his room was steadily filling with ash and pumice. Eventually his servants had to wake him to save him from being trapped inside. Then began a discussion about what the occupants of the villa should do – stay put or take their chances in the open? The villa was frequently being shaken by earth tremors which had already brought down some buildings, but outside large lumps of pumice were falling. Finally, they decided to go out and see if conditions were suitable for putting to sea, but before doing so they tied pillows to their heads to protect them from the falling lumps of pumice. What happened then by the shore is recorded in Pliny the Younger's letter to Tacitus:

Ancient Romans killed by the AD *79 eruption of Vesuvius. Their bodies decomposed under the hot ash, leaving hollows that were discovered during excavations 1900 years later. These were filled with plaster of Paris to make the casts shown here.*

His slaves put down a sheet for him to lie on and he asked for and drank one or two cups of cold water. Then the flames and the smell of sulphur, which always tells you the flames are coming, made the others run away. These flames made him wake up. He stood up, leaning on two young slaves, but he fell down straight away. I suppose the thick fumes had blocked his windpipe and closed his gullet which was always weak and giving him trouble. When they found his body in the light two days later, there was not a mark on it. He still had his clothes on. He looked like a man asleep, not a man who had died.

From this description there are several possible causes for the death of Pliny the Elder. The fact that he had to lie down and ask for water implies that he was feeling unwell. Being rather stout, it is possible that he simply died of a heart attack, but the 'weak gullet' could mean that he suffered from asthma and that he died from a severe asthmatic attack brought on by the heavy ashfall and thick fumes. He could also have died from inhaling too much dust and acid gas to which he might have been more susceptible than the others. However, the mention of flames arriving and the smell of sulphur are puzzling. 'Flames' could refer to St Elmo's fire, an electrical phenomenon commonly associated with large pyroclastic eruptions such as Krakatoa (see p. 9), but it is also possible that the group were on the edge of a nuée ardente. It is not explicitly stated when the others abandoned Pliny, so they might have escaped its lethal effects while he was caught and overcome.

Meanwhile, the younger Pliny and his mother were still at Misenum, more than 18 miles (30 km) from Vesuvius. After his uncle had left, Pliny continued with his studies for the rest of the afternoon, had supper with his mother and went to bed. He fell into an uneasy sleep, for the earthquakes, which had been so frequent in the preceding weeks and years as to be considered quite normal, now became particularly violent. Before dawn his mother woke him and they decided to go into the courtyard for safety. When dawn came, the light was very feeble, but in a Roman gesture reminiscent of his uncle's, Pliny got out a book to show his calmness and began writing notes.

A friend then burst in and advised them to leave the

town at once as the buildings might fall at any moment and crush them. The earthquakes were now so strong and continuous that stationary chariots could not be kept from running away, even when the wheels were chocked with large stones. The tremors were also causing tsunamis and the sea kept retreating out into the bay, leaving sea creatures stranded on the shore. On the other side of the bay they could see a terrible black cloud which had lightning flashing within it and glowing masses of flame behind it – like sheet lightning but much bigger. At this their friend again urged them to leave, but they did not want to without knowing the fate of the elder Pliny, so their friend left in desperation. Soon afterwards the dark cloud descended over the sea, covering the island of Capri and the promontory of Misenum nearby.

There was then a frantic argument between Pliny and his mother. She begged him to leave while he could, but refused to do so herself, saying she was overweight and too old to run and would slow him down. Pliny staunchly refused to leave his mother and she was eventually persuaded to accompany him, though with great reluctance. A light fall of ashes now began and they could see the dense black cloud following them. There was a panicking crowd on the road, so they turned off it into the open as the cloud overtook them. Suddenly, they were plunged into pitch black, darker than the darkest night.

In this horrific darkness screams and shouts of terror could be heard all around. Men and women were calling for their children, children were screaming for their parents, while others just wished to die quickly. Most were convinced that the end of the world had come – that this was the final darkness which would never end. Pliny certainly thought so and found some small comfort in the fact that at least he was perishing in company with all mankind. It then grew rather lighter, but this was only the approach of flames, and complete darkness followed again.

Pliny does not say how long this darkness lasted, but eventually, presumably the same day (25 August), a feeble light began to return and even the sun could be dimly seen. The landscape had changed completely. Everything was now covered with ash so deep that it looked like snow. Pliny and his mother returned to Misenum, where even the following night they found sleep difficult because of continuing earthquakes.

Although Pliny's account of this eruption was motivated only by personal reasons, it can also claim to be scientific because he stuck to the facts and refused to embellish what he saw. This type of eruption is now universally known as plinian in his honour.

In comparison with areas nearer to Vesuvius, Misenum escaped lightly. Pompeii, some 6 miles (10 km) from the volcano, was buried in 15–25 ft (5–8 metres) of ash and pumice. Herculaneum, only 4 miles (7 km) from Vesuvius, was buried by a very deep lahar (mudflow), up to 65 ft (20 metres) thick in places. While devastating at the time, the mud has been of enormous value to archaeologists as it helped to preserve buildings and artefacts that other volcanic material would certainly have destroyed. It also allowed much of the population time to get away. Only a handful of skeletons have been found, most of them in a building on the waterfront, but at Pompeii 2000 skeletons have been discovered. Interestingly, the consolidation of ash allowed the bodies to decompose leaving a hollow space with the bones inside. The most recently discovered of these hollows have been filled with plaster of Paris and the resulting casts are remarkable, in some cases preserving facial expressions and details of clothing.

Although parts of Pompeii and Herculaneum must have poked above their coverings of ash and mud, both towns were quickly overgrown and forgotten, remaining so for the next 1600 years. In fact, by the end of the second century AD the eruption had already been distorted into legend. An account by Xiphilinus describes the AD 79 eruption in terms of giants wandering over the land and trumpets sounding, though he does mention the destruction of Pompeii and Herculaneum, and the interesting observation that dust from this eruption not only darkened the sky in Rome but also travelled as far as Africa, Syria and Egypt.

After this eruption, Vesuvius became a more regularly active volcano again, with important eruptions in 472, which spread ashes all over Europe, and 1036. After an eruption in 1139 the volcano seems to have been very quiet until a huge eruption in 1631, which included strong explosions, several lava flows and lahars. Six towns were destroyed by lava and nine wrecked by mudflows. From 1631 to 1944 Vesuvius went through cycles of activity in which five to ten years of repose were followed by the appearance of cinder cones on the crater floor. Strombolian activity from these cones, together with intermittent lava flows, gradually filled up the crater to the top. Pressure built up within the crater and a final eruption started. Earthquakes began and the sides of the cone split. Floods of lava poured out and there were frequent, massive 'gas blow-offs', the most dramatic being that of April 1906, which was essentially a continuous explosion lasting two days. This removed much of the central cone, which lost 325 ft (100 metres) in height. This marked the end of the cycle and was followed by a few years of repose again.

The last of these cycles of activity ended with the culminating eruption of 1944, and Vesuvius has been totally inactive ever since. An exuberant account of this last eruption is given by the comedian Spike Milligan in volume five of his war memoirs, *Where Have All the Bullets Gone?*. It makes a strange but somehow appropriate comparison with the account by Pliny the Younger, also a non-volcanologist. Spike Milligan was in a cinema watching a Gracie Fields film when the final gas blow-off phase began. Exhibiting calmness that would have impressed the ancient Romans, he drove through the panic to the foot of the volcano, bought two bottles of wine and spent the night watching the eruption from the ruins of Pompeii!

ETNA, 1669

The Etna eruption of 1669 was not violent and caused no deaths, but it was extremely destructive and had widespread economic effects on the region. It is also famous as the first eruption in which an attempt was made to divert the course of a lava flow.

The eruption began on 11 March after two weeks of earthquakes, when a fissure 6 miles (10 km) long opened down the south side of Mount Etna. Lava poured out, accompanied by strombolian explosions at several points along the fissure, but the activity soon merged into one major cone, Monti Rossi, which built up rapidly next to the village of Nicolosi, 9 miles (15 km) south of the summit. Although the village was damaged by volcanic bombs, the lava streams passed to the west and rapidly spread downslope. The following day they had already wiped out the town of Belpasso, 2½ miles (4 km) from Monti Rossi, and showed no signs of abating. The following day the lava reached

Mount Vesuvius today. It has not erupted since 1944, and is now a popular tourist attraction overlooking the Bay of Naples.

Mascalucia, San Pietro and Camporotundo, all of which were destroyed or suffered major damage.

By 12 April the lava had travelled 9 miles (15 km) and was at the gates of Catania, the second largest city in Sicily and an important port for the island, so an attempt was made to divert the flow. Fifty men, protecting themselves against the heat of the lava by covering themselves with wet cowhides, used picks and iron bars to hack away at the sides of the flow, where it had formed a cooling crust. They succeeded in opening a breach in the flow walls from which the hotter fluid lava inside began to emerge at right angles to the main direction of flow. Hearing of the diversion attempt and fearing that the lava would be diverted to threaten their town, Paternò – a ridiculous fear as it was 12 miles (20 km) away and uphill – 500 of the inhabitants turned up with trumpets and drums and succeeded in stopping the diversion attempt.

The walls of Catania were breached by the flow on 30 April, destroying all the western part of the town, including the Roman amphitheatre, and flowing into the sea, filling the harbour and creating a new promontory. When the eruption finally stopped in the middle of July, it had covered 13½ square miles (35 square km) of farmland and partially or totally wiped out fifteen towns and villages. Some of these were reconstructed on the same sites, but some have never been rebuilt.

VULCANO, 1888

Like Etna, the island of Vulcano was held by some of the ancients to be the home of Vulcan, god of fire and metal-workers. This gave the island its name, and when later writers described its activity more accurately, the name came to be applied to all mountains of the same type and thus the word volcano was born.

Vulcano is one of the Aeolian Islands, a group of volcanoes situated in the Mediterranean 60 miles (100 km) north of Mount Etna. It appears to have been much more active in ancient times than now and was

The eruption of Mount Etna in 1669, as it might have been painted by a contemporary artist. The view shows the city of Catania, most of which was destroyed as the lava flowed over it into the sea.

also fairly active in the eighteenth century, being in a continuous state of eruption for periods of ten years or more. In 1786 a very big eruption occurred, which terrified the population of the neighbouring islands. In fact, the southern part of Vulcano itself, which had been farmed and inhabited since ancient times, was abandoned altogether.

There then followed a period of dormancy so long that many thought Vulcano had become extinct. But in 1873, several fissures opened in the crater floor and strong vapour emission occurred for eighteen months, accompanied by the ejection of bombs. This was but a small prelude to later developments.

On 3 August 1888 Vulcano's most famous eruption began. Over a two-year period strong explosions occurred, accompanied by dense, dark clouds of ash, but no lava or nuées were ever emitted. The explosions were so violent that windows were broken in the town of Lipari, nearly 5 miles (8 km) away, and quantities of pumice and incandescent rocks, some 6–10 ft (2–3 metres) across, were scattered over the crater and its surroundings. At first, most of the ejected blocks were of old lavas and it seemed that the eruption had removed a plug of older material blocking the crater. This initial vent-clearing was then followed by the ejection of ash, bombs and scoria composed of new magmatic material. A submarine cable from Lipari to Sicily was broken four times during this period, the last time in 1892, so activity must also have occurred much lower down the slopes beneath the sea.

The eruption was well observed by a number of people, including Mercalli (the same man who devised a scale of earthquake intensities), and since it did not fit the characteristics of any known eruption type, it became the prototype for vulcanian eruptions (see p. 75) which, along with hawaiian, strombolian and plinian, forms one of the four major classes of volcanic eruption. Thus, Vulcano is a double classic, not only providing the prototype for all volcanoes, but for an important type of activity as well.

10
FAMOUS MODERN ERUPTIONS

MOUNT KATMAI, 1912

Lying near the south coast of Alaska opposite Kodiak Island, Mount Katmai was not known to be active before 1912. On 2 June in that year earthquakes were felt at Katmai village, 15 miles (25 km) south of the volcano, and quite strong shocks on 4 and 5 June. These were ignored, however, as Alaska suffers destructive earthquakes quite frequently. On the evening of 5 June people 40 miles (65 km) away noticed a strange black cloud over Mount Katmai, but no one realized it was a volcanic eruption.

It was therefore a complete surprise when, the following day at one o'clock, there was a deafening explosion heard up to 730 miles (1200 km) away. This produced a dense ash cloud which resulted in total darkness over the region. The cloud reached Kodiak, 98 miles (160 km) to the southeast, late that afternoon, producing a rain of ashes with the darkness. A second tremendous explosion occurred at 11 p.m. By the following morning the ash was 5 in (12 cm) deep at Kodiak, and at noon ash began to fall again with renewed vigour, eventually accumulating to a depth of 10 in (25 cm) and causing pitch darkness and heavy electrostatic disturbances which made radios go dead. Sulphurous fumes could also be smelt and avalanches of ashes descended the neighbouring hills.

A ship in the Shelikof Strait, only 50 miles (80 km) from Mount Katmai, suffered much heavier ashfalls, which accumulated on deck and clung thickly to the sides and undersides of objects. Ash quickly penetrated the pilot-house, making it very difficult for the helmsman to see the compass in front of him. Lightning flashes and thunderclaps were continuous, and St Elmo's fire was visible on the ship itself. Meanwhile, the temperature rose steadily until the heat was stifling, and at intervals birds fell helpless on the deck.

At 10.40 p.m. on 7 June there was a third colossal explosion, after which the activity ceased, though

The Valley of Ten Thousand Smokes. Caves were found in a huge, ash-covered snowdrift caused by the hot fumaroles (seen here as crevasses) melting the snow from below.

minor eruptions continued during the rest of the summer. No one had experienced the eruption at close quarters, and it was for this reason alone that no one was killed. Closest of all to the volcano were a group of natives at Kafia Bay, just over 25 miles (40 km) to the east. They were in constant darkness for three days and had to feel their way around with lighted lamps, unaware of whether it was day or night. One of them wrote to his wife on 9 June describing the thunder and noise, and telling her that the ashes were more than 10 ft (3 metres) deep in places, covering all the rivers, so that they had no water and were awaiting death at any moment.

The National Geographic Society immediately organized an expedition to Mount Katmai, which arrived there four weeks after the eruption. They found that the top of Mount Katmai had disappeared, leaving a caldera nearly 3 miles (5 km) wide, in the bottom of which lay a lake more than ½ mile (1 km) below the original summit. In all, an astonishing 1½ cubic miles (6 cubic km) of rock had been removed. The western wall was an amazing sight, being made of sheer ice cliffs, for the old summit had been covered with glaciers, now truncated by the eruption. However, the most extraordinary discovery was not made on the first, but on the third expedition to the volcano in 1916. Before the 1912 eruption, a well-known trail went through a valley of the Ukak River northwest of Mount Katmai. It was a valley rich in plant and animal life, but when the expedition arrived there they found that the 15-mile (25-km) long valley had been filled with hot sand to make a level plain 50 square miles (130 square km) in extent, from which thousands of jets of steam and acid gases issued at temperatures up to 650°C. The explorers said that the sound of these high-pressure fumaroles was like 'all the steam engines in the world letting off steam in concert', and they named the place the Valley of Ten Thousand Smokes,

This valley was an exciting and important discovery, for in the ensuing years it became clear that it had been filled with a deposit often seen in the strata of old volcanoes and always assumed to be some strange kind of lava. However, the deposit in the Valley of Ten Thousand Smokes was clearly not a lava, but had been emplaced in a fluidized flow similar to a nuée ardente from Mount Pelée (see p. 15), but on a much larger scale. It had come not from Mount Katmai itself, but from a series of long fissures about 5 miles (9 km) to the northwest, the largest of which was named Novarupta. It had swept down the valley at lightning speed in the earliest stages of the eruption, destroying and burying everything in its path. This type of deposit was eventually named an ignimbrite, and eruptions which produce them are the largest and most explosive type known.

PARICUTIN, 1943

The eruption of Paricutín volcano, named after a village nearby, was particularly dramatic because it began in an ordinary cornfield. This was owned by a local farmer, Dionisio Pulido, and contained a small pit which, even fifty years before, children playing inside had found pleasantly warm. On the morning of 5 February 1943, after two weeks of earthquakes had shaken the area, Dionisio arrived at the field with his wife, son and a neighbour to prepare it for planting. At 4.00 p.m. he noticed a small fissure passing through the pit and soon after there was a thunderous noise, the trees shook and the ground rose about 6 ft (2 metres). Dust and fumes began rising from the fissure, followed by the loud, continuous hiss of escaping gas and the strong smell of sulphur. When glowing rocks began to be hurled out and trees 100 ft (30 metres) away caught fire, they hurriedly departed.

In the early evening, watching from the village of San Juan de Parangaricutiro 2 miles (3 km) away, they could see that larger bombs were being thrown out, though as yet there was no noise. Around midnight a roaring noise accompanied the ejection of huge bombs into the air, and lightning flashes appeared in the thick ash column. By midday the following day, a cone 165 ft (50 metres) high had built up, which grew to 460 ft (140 metres) after a week and 1060 ft (325 metres) after a year.

Dionisio and his companions had witnessed what few humans have ever seen – the birth of a volcano – and this was the initial stage of an eruption that lasted nine years and twelve days. Activity reached its peak in 1944, when lava destroyed the villages of Paricutín and San Juan de Parangaricutiro, only the church tower poking out above the flow indicating that the latter village had ever existed. This eruption is probably the first and last from this volcano, one of about fifty similar old volcanoes within a 6-mile (10-km) radius of Paricutín.

OVERLEAF: *Glowing lava from Paricutín engulfs the town of San Juan de Parangaricutiro in June 1944. Only the church steeple stands.*

MOUNT LAMINGTON, 1951

Situated on the eastern peninsula of Papua New Guinea, far from any large towns, Mount Lamington was not known to be a volcano before the 1951 eruption. There are several small settlements on and around the mountain, however, and on 15 January earthquakes were felt and villagers saw avalanches near the summit and vapour rising from the crater. Three days later a column of ash rose more than ½ mile (1 km) high, and in Higaturu, the nearest settlement 6 miles (10 km) north of the summit, ground movements became almost continuous. On 19 January some spectacular electric displays were seen and next day the ash column reached a height of about 5 miles (8 km). Unfortunately, none of these warnings were understood or heeded by the villagers.

The first catastrophic explosions began at 10.40 a.m. on 21 January, producing an enormous, mushroom-shaped cloud that rose to 7 miles (12 km) in two minutes and reached over 9 miles (15 km) in twenty minutes. The base of the cloud expanded with lightning speed to envelop the whole mountain, and was accompanied by a continuous roar that could be heard 195 miles (320 km) away. A second violent outburst occurred at 8.45 that night, and between quieter periods further explosive phases occurred on 25 January, 6 and 18 February and 5 March. Similar but milder outbursts followed from time to time, and the growth of a dome within the crater continued for nearly two years.

The effect of this activity was disastrous. A massive nuée ardente travelling at 60 mph (100 kph) accompanied the original paroxysm of 21 January, totally destroying everything within an area of 60 square miles (150 square km), carrying away whole buildings, removing all rain forest and even tree stumps. The loss of life totalled 2942, and even outside the zone of total destruction many were killed by heat scarring the lungs and body, though those in well-constructed rooms survived.

BEZYMIANNY, 1956

Once regarded as extinct, even though surrounded by active volcanoes of similar type, Bezymianny volcano in Kamchatka, USSR, surprised everyone in 1955 when earthquakes were recorded beneath it. On 22 October in the same year vulcanian ash explosions began which, by 17 November, were so strong that in Kliuchi, 28 miles (45 km) away, visibility was reduced to 170 yards (150 metres). Moderate activity continued until 30 March 1956, when an extraordinary event happened, which was not fully understood until much later.

At 5.11 p.m. a catastrophic explosion accompanied the total removal of the top of the cone, though in contrast to other eruptions, this was fairly silent, only muffled rumblings being heard. The initial blast was directed sideways to the east. A huge black cloud rose from the volcano, quickly curling and changing its outlines, and rapidly reaching 28 miles (45 km) high. At Kliuchi the cloud rapidly approached, with a growing rumble of thunder and continuous lightning flashes hitting the town at 5.40. Darkness ensued, with a strong smell of sulphur, and dust fell so densely that visibility was reduced to zero. People were stumbling about looking for their own homes and the deafening noise of thunder was incessantly crashing all around. The air was thick with electricity, causing telephones to ring spontaneously and loudspeakers to burn out.

Tall trees were flattened over a distance of 15 miles (25 km) and went up in flames 18 miles (29 km) from Bezymianny. Hot ash, deposited over an area of 195 square miles (500 square km), caused snow-melt and lahars, some of which travelled 56 miles (90 km). A huge pyroclastic flow 15 miles (24 km) long spread from the volcano, but was so mobile and charged with gas that it could not remain on the steep slopes and appeared to start at the foot of the volcano. Thanks to thousands of hissing steam fumaroles, the area was promptly named the Valley of Ten Thousand Smokes of Kamchatka.

Bezymianny had suffered a sector collapse similar to that of Mount St Helens in 1980, though this was only fully appreciated later. The air wave from the blast could be detected 40 miles (65 km) away as a strong pressure in the ears, and recording barographs around the world recorded its passage as it circled the Earth one and a half times.

TRISTAN DA CUNHA, 1962

The eruption on Tristan da Cunha Island in 1962 seems rather pathetic compared with the dramatic eruptions described on the previous pages. None the less, it had a traumatic effect on the population for very different reasons, changing forever this small, isolated community. The tiny island, less than 6 miles (10 km) across, is one of the most remote places in the world,

Bezymianny volcano, Kamchatka. The 'ghost' outline shows it shape before the sector collapse of 30 March 1956.

being situated in the middle of the South Atlantic about 1800 miles (3000 km) from South Africa and nearly 2500 miles (4000 km) from South America. It had been claimed by the British, and in 1817 a small group of Scottish and English settlers established a farming community that had no contact with the outside world, except through the occasional passing ship. The island lies on the Mid-Atlantic Ridge, so it was perhaps inevitable that an eruption would occur sooner or later.

When, in 1961, the old volcano which forms the bulk of the island sprang into life, the inhabitants radioed for help, and it was quickly decided that the 264 islanders should be evacuated to England, where homes were found for them in Hampshire. They had led a simple life without any system of money and spoke the language of 1817 almost unchanged. They also retained many nineteenth-century opinions and habits, so the shock of arriving in twentieth-century England was devastating.

When scientists returned to the volcano a few months later, they found little damage, apart from a small lava flow, and the cows which had been left behind were grazing peacefully, apparently unaffected by the events which had so traumatized their owners. It was deemed safe for the islanders to return, and in 1963 a majority voted to go back, though some of the younger ones had married English people and opted to stay behind.

Once back on Tristan da Cunha, it became clear that twentieth-century life had subtly altered the islanders' outlook. Although they carried on much as before – growing potatoes and apples, keeping cattle, sheep and geese, and catching fish and lobsters – money and wages were soon introduced and inevitably their once idyllic existence changed forever.

HELGAFELL, 1973

Like Tristan da Cunha, Helgafell is on the Mid-Atlantic Ridge, but lies some 7000 miles (11,000 km) further north, on the island of Vestmannaeyjar off the coast of Iceland. It had not erupted for 6000 years when, in the early hours of 23 January 1973, a fissure opened

Evacuees leave their cottages on Tristan da Cunha in the South Atlantic as the island's volcanic vent steams menacingly behind them.

Helgafell erupting in 1973 above the fishing port of Heimaey on Vestmannaeyjar island, just off the south coast of Iceland. Successful attempts were made to limit the lava damage by cooling the flow with water.

Cross-sections of Mount St Helens volcano during the sector collapse of 18 May 1980. **1** *The rising magma pushes the north flank of the mountain outwards.*

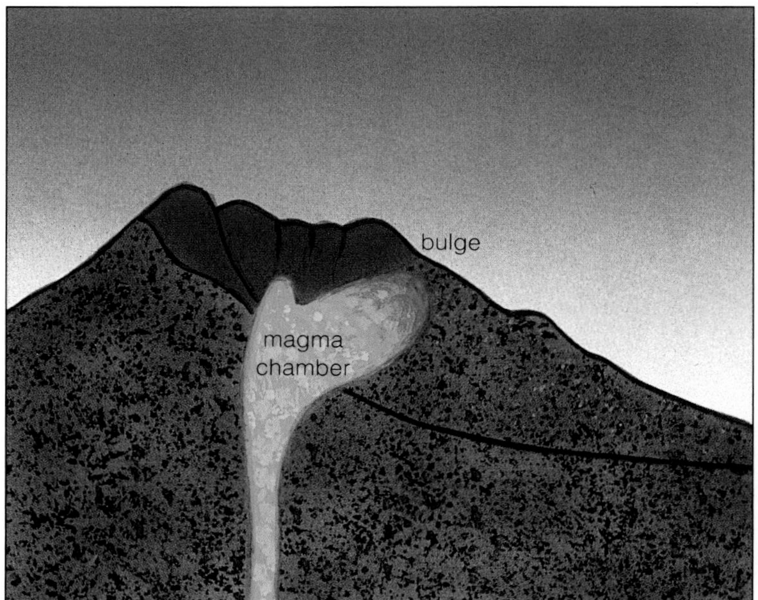

2 *The flank becomes unstable and a huge section starts to slide downslope, laying bare part of the magma, which is suddenly depressurized and starts to degas explosively.*

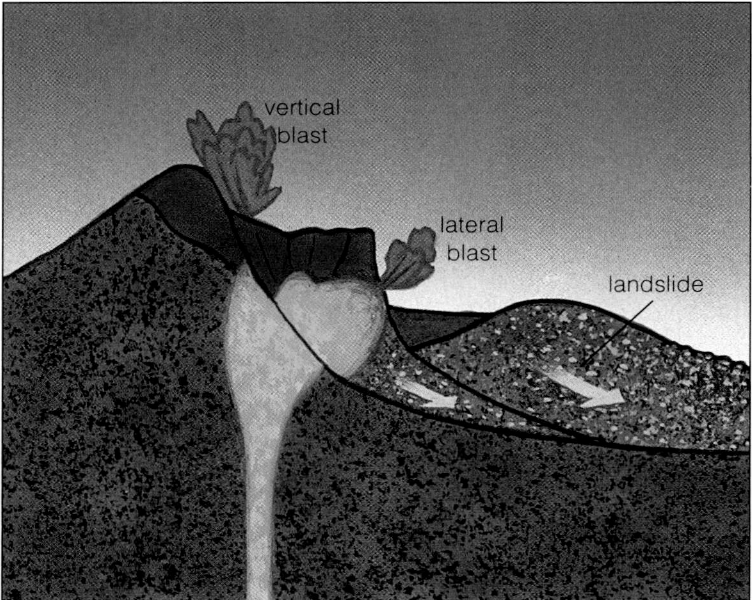

which quickly lengthened to more than 1 mile (2 km), cutting through the island from one side to the other, emitting lava and spraying a continuous curtain of fire. The population of Heimaey, the town very close to Helgafell, was immediately evacuated and ash quickly covered houses on the western edge of the town.

Activity concentrated at a point northeast of Helgafell itself and a cinder cone grew here which, by the end of February, was 650 ft (200 metres) in height. The town of Heimaey is one of the major fishing ports of Iceland, so when lavas threatened the harbour upon which the fishing industry depended, an attempt was made to limit the damage by cooling the flow with water (see p. 158). This appears to have been successful, and by the end of the eruption in June, the new lavas had created a sea wall which made an even better harbour than before the eruption.

MOUNT ST HELENS, 1980

No volcanic eruption had occurred on the mainland of the USA (excluding Alaska) since 1916, so when Mount St Helens in Washington State began erupting steam and ash on 27 March 1980, after more than a week of earthquakes, America looked forward to a real spectacle. Some 360 people living on or near the volcano were evacuated, but one old man, Harry Truman, who lived by Spirit Lake 6 miles (10 km) north of the summit, refused to leave his home. Volcanologists from all over the USA flocked to this eruption on their doorstep, bringing equipment of all kinds to ensure that this would be the best-observed eruption of its kind ever. As the explosions grew stronger, ash fell as far as 215 miles (350 km) away by the end of March, reaching a distance of 300 miles (500 km) in early April.

In mid April it was noticed that the northern flank had a strange appearance. Air photographs showed that a huge bulge up to 300 ft (100 metres) high had appeared there since the beginning of the eruption. This bulge continued to grow at rates which approached the incredible speed of 6 ft (2 metres) a day, while the summit above the bulge was subsiding. The possibility that a major landslide of horrific dimensions might take place here was frequently discussed, but apparently not considered imminent. Consequently, lumberjacks who had been banned from working on the mountain were allowed back into the danger zone on 18 May at 9.00 a.m.

Early on the morning of the 18th two sightseers drove up a neighbouring peak to photograph the volcano. The weather was perfect – clear and still. Shortly after 8 a.m. they had the camera set up on a tripod and began taking pictures. At 8.32, as one of them had his binoculars trained on the volcano, there was a magnitude 5 earthquake. A little later it seemed as if the ground above the bulge on the north side was becoming blurred, then the bulge itself began to separate from the mountain along a fissure that opened above it. The bulge quickly formed a massive avalanche that raced downslope, hit Spirit Lake, smacked into a ridge 5 miles (8 km) to the north and turned west down the Toutle River valley.

The two sightseers could not believe their luck; they

3 *More of the magma is laid bare, and a major lateral and vertical blast develops.*

4 *The blast rapidly leads to a huge pyroclastic eruption.*

took twenty-one spectacular photographs of the cataclysm in quick succession before suddenly realizing that they too were in danger from the powerful, laterally-directed blast that raced outward and overtook the avalanche within seconds. Hastily grabbing the camera, they jumped into their vehicle and raced downhill at breakneck speed. As they neared the bottom of the hill away from the volcano, they met the blast and pyroclastic flow coming round the side, cutting them off and giving off intolerable heat. After a series of adventures, in which they abandoned their vehicle, they managed to escape with the camera. At great risk to their lives they had saved a priceless pictorial record of the early stages of the eruption.

The avalanche removed at least ¼ cubic mile (1 cubic km) from the top of the mountain, lowering its height by about 1150 ft (350 metres). The blast detroyed everything in a zone about 6 miles (10 km) long, and outside this the trees were flattened, pointing away from the volcano in a radial pattern. Altogether, fifty-seven people are known to have died, or are missing presumed dead, including Dr David Johnston, a young volcanologist on duty 5 miles (8 km) north of the summit, one of the few volcanologists ever to have been killed during an eruption. The victims nearest the volcano were buried without trace under the pyroclastic flows that followed the catastrophic slope failure, and those furthest away died from suffocation when heat scalded their lungs.

The eruption cloud rose above the tropopause to an altitude of 12 miles (19 km), and on the ground pyroclastic flows raced northwards, fanning out to cover the remains of Spirit Lake and the Toutle River. The avalanche and pyroclastic flow created mudflows which destroyed 123 homes and virtually all the Toutle River bridges for many miles downstream, then continued into the Cowlitz and Columbia rivers, where mud, debris and logs clogged the ship channel and stranded many boats at Portland harbour.

Weather satellites show the progress of the ash cloud, initially in all directions, then eastwards, reaching the east coast of America in three days, and completely circling the Earth in eleven days. The ashfall affected much of the USA; at Yakima, 85 miles (140 km) downwind, the ash was nearly 1 in (2 cm) deep, and the automatic street lighting came on at 11.15 a.m. and did not go off until the following morning. The economic cost of this eruption, including losses to financial enterprises, tourism and cleaning up, totalled nearly $3 billion.

The 18 May cataclysm marked a turning point in the understanding of this type of eruption, for the superb series of photographs enable the progress of sector collapse to be followed in great detail for the first time. Although this first event was not predicted, the subsequent behaviour of the dome that appeared within the amphitheatre-shaped crater that remained showed a repeated series of events before each of the explosions that followed. As a result, volcanologists became quite adept at predicting explosions with an accuracy of an hour or two. These explosions continued at intervals of a few weeks to a few months, with decreasing intensity, for a couple of years. The last appearance of fresh lava from the dome was in 1986.

Mount St Helens shortly after the start of the 18 May 1980 eruption, seen from a peak a few miles to the northeast.

NEVADO DEL RUIZ, 1985

Ruiz volcano is a large, shield-shaped structure situated in the Andes. At 17,680 ft (5390 metres), it is the highest active volcano in Colombia, with glaciers and thick deposits of ice and snow around the summit. Two particularly devastating historic eruptions, those of 1595 and 1845, both resulted in destructive lahars and loss of life.

Local earthquakes were detected in the summit area in late November 1984, and these increased at the end of December, when rises in fumarole temperature at the summit occurred and small phreatic explosions began. Seismic and thermal activity both increased throughout the first half of 1985 and strong gas emission was noticed during a visit to the summit in July. The glaciers were also starting to melt in some places, causing the level of the lake in the crater to rise by about 3 ft (1 metre). A seven-hour emission of ash from the summit crater began on 11 September at midday, accompanied by continuous roaring and electrical discharges. Blocks were ejected on to the summit snowfields as far as 1 mile (2 km) from the crater. A lahar left the summit area in the late afternoon and ran for 17 miles (27 km) down the River Azufrado on the northeast flank. In some places along the way mud rose as much as 65 ft (20 metres) up the canyon walls.

These were very strong warning signs, so a hazard map was prepared by an international team of volcanologists and distributed to Red Cross and Civil Defence officials. This showed quite clearly that the town of Armero, which lay further downstream, was in danger of destruction by lahars. Despite this clear-cut advice, the valley residents were 'placed on alert' but were not evacuated.

Two days after the 11 September activity changes in the shape of the glaciers on the west side could be seen and new cracks in the ice north of the summit had appeared near a small, growing pond. Phreatic activity, emitting variable emounts of ash, continued for the rest of September, but declined in October. Then, on 7 November, seismic activity began again, though there were fewer earthquake swarms than before the 11 September ash emission. Continuous volcanic tremor began on 10 November but, again, this was not so strong as the tremor before 11 September.

Eruptive activity began again at 3.45 p.m. on the afternoon of 13 November. There was bad weather with heavy rain all around, so no one could see exactly what was going on, but fifteen minutes later ash fell at Mariquita, 37 miles (59 km) northeast of the summit, and nearly two hours later ash and lapilli were falling at Armero, 28 miles (46 km) slightly further to the east-northeast. A volcanologist looking after seismic equipment only 5½ miles (9 km) from the summit, where it was pouring with rain, heard nothing until after 9 p.m. at night, when strong explosions, much louder than those of 11 September, shook the building and lit up the rain clouds. Half an hour later lumps of pumice 6 in (15 cm) across were falling. At 10 p.m. the ashfall at Armero increased and twenty minutes later a cargo plane, unaware of what was happening, flew through the eruption cloud at an altitude of 5 miles (8 km). Its windscreen was pelted with ash and pumice, and so badly scratched that the pilot could not see out. After two failed attempts to land at Bogotá, he managed to get the plane down safely at Cali by flying with his head out of a side window.

This explosive activity rapidly melted at least 5 per cent of the ice at the summit and also disrupted the lakes that had been growing for a year. An enormous body of water was discharged, which raced down the volcano, soon combining with the ash and pumice to create a wall of mud racing down the river valleys at 18–22 mph (30–35 kph). One of these lahars hit the town of Armero just after 11.30 p.m., killing over three-quarters of its 25,000 population. Another hit the low-lying parts of Chinchina, on the opposite side of Ruiz, killing about 1000. The mud was not hot, so some of those who were swept downstream by the lahars miraculously survived; in fact, a few were rescued alive up to three days after the tragedy, but there was little comfort for these survivors. Nearly all of them, including many children, had lost the rest of their families, and their homes and livelihood had been destroyed.

This was the fourth worst death toll of any eruption known in history, yet all the warning signs were there and were correctly interpreted by the volcanologists who had studied the activity for a year before disaster struck. Despite this perfectly adequate surveillance and advice, and the great length of time available for evacuation, the relevant authorities adopted a 'wait and see' policy with appalling results. In a terribly ironic move, 15,000 people were evacuated from low-lying areas all around the volcano after an increase in earthquakes on 3 January. This, however, proved to be unnecessary, as the activity resulted in only small explosions and ashfall, so most people returned to their homes after two days.

The aftermath of the disastrous lahars of 13 November 1985 from Nevado del Ruiz volcano, Colombia. A total of 22,000 people were killed.

11 CONTINUOUSLY ACTIVE VOLCANOES

STROMBOLI

Out of 500 or so active volcanoes in the world, about a dozen are continuously active in the sense that they usually have a molten lava lake or daily explosive activity at the summit, and about the same number have eruptions every year or two, so they are also considered virtually continuous. Stromboli is one of the best known examples of the former, with strombolian explosions at the summit a few times per hour on average, and occasional lava flows too. It has shown similar activity for at least the past 2000 years.

The island of Stromboli, off the northeast coast of Sicily, measures only 2 x 2½ miles (3 x 4 km). The summit is 3000 ft (900 metres) above sea level, but it represents the top of a much bigger volcano that lies mostly beneath the sea. Its continuous and relatively safe activity has made it a favourite tourist attraction and several boats a day carry sightseers to the town of San Vincenzo, from where a well-trodden path leads to the summit. This is the best observation point, being 500 ft (150 metres) higher than the active cones, which can be seen below to the northwest. There appears to have been a sector collapse on this side in the past, marked by the Sciara del Fuoco, a horseshoe-shaped valley more than ½ mile (1 km) across, now partly filled with the active cones and the steep lavas which have accumulated from them.

Episodes of increased activity at Stromboli are relatively few and far between, the most recent occurrences being in 1975 and 1985–86, when lava flowed down the Sciara del Fuoco. In 1985 there was a short but violent explosive phase, and even a small nuée ardente that hit the sea. The most violent explosive phase at Stromboli, however, was in 1930 when, in the early morning of 11 September, a dark cloud of ashes appeared above the crater without warning. All was quiet for more than an hour, then suddenly there were two extremely loud explosions in quick succession which could be heard more than 40 miles (60 km) away. Blocks weighing 30 tons (30.5 tonnes) were hurled up to 2 miles (3 km) away and some houses were destroyed in Ginostra, only 1 mile (2 km) away. Tsunami 6 ft (2 metres) in height accompanied the explosions, which were followed by a small, hot avalanche, possibly a nuée ardente, which killed four people. One was scalded to death in the boiling seawater near where the avalanche reached the coast.

LEFT: Stromboli volcano in an unusually active period, with lava flows pouring down the Sciara del Fuoco, creating vast steam clouds as they enter the sea.

KILAUEA, HAWAII

Although it has more than one eruption per year, Kilauea on Hawaii is inactive between eruptions, so at present must be classed as almost continually active. However, it does go through long periods of continuous activity. For example, it was in continuous eruption between 1969 and 1974, and again from 1983 to the present. It is also known that until 1924 there had been a molten lava lake within Halemaumau, the pit within the summit caldera, which had existed even before the first missionaires arrived in 1820. Such lava lakes are a spectacular sight and can still be seen occasionally today. There was one inside Halemaumau for eight months during the 1967–68 eruption, and often within Mauna Ulu during the 1969–74 eruption. During these times changes in lava lake level are common; a slowly increasing level can produce levees (embankments) as the edge solidifies, so that the lake is confined to a raised pool within the crater. A sudden increase in lava level will produce an overflow, while a sudden drop may drain the lake altogether. The thin, solidified surface of the lake behaves rather like the crust of the Earth; rising convective currents develop and separate solidified plates floating on the surface provide beautiful small-scale analogues of plate tectonics and continental drift, including spreading axes, subduction zones and transform faults.

Like Stromboli, the Hawaiian volcanoes have long been a tourist attraction, as the frequent activity and floods of lava that often pour from them can produce the most spectacular scenes such as the lava cascades pictured overleaf. They have also attracted scientists, and Kilauea in particular has acted as something of a 'laboratory volcano' for eighty years, ever since the Hawaiian Volcano Observatory (HVO) was established there to provide a permanent scientific monitoring system. Although this was by no means the first volcano observatory to be set up (the Vesuvius Observatory was founded in 1842), the dual advantages of a

OVERLEAF: Spectacular lava cascades pour over the cliffs of a collapse crater, as very fluid lavas erupt from Mauna Ulu cone on Kilauea volcano, Hawaii.

properly financed observatory and a volcano which is in eruption most years has meant that the HVO has contributed more to our understanding of active volcanoes than any other establishment.

MOUNT ETNA, SICILY

The largest active volcano in Europe, Mount Etna measures 25 miles (40 km) across the base and rises to 10,990 ft (3317 metres) above sea level, although this height varies as the summit undergoes both upbuilding and collapse. Like Stromboli, it is one of the few volcanoes that can truly be described as continuously active, for strombolian explosions have been occurring at the summit every few seconds or minutes since 1536 at least, and probably since ancient times.

Thanks to its position at the heart of the ancient world, Etna has a longer written record of eruptive activity than any other volcano. Although its continuous activity has meant that many smaller eruptions have been ignored, dates and details of over 200 eruptions have been recorded back to 695 BC and there are also imprecise references to an earlier big eruption around 1500 BC. Throughout this long period there is nothing to suggest that its behaviour has changed significantly from the present-day activity.

This long record of reliability has meant that tourism is an important source of livelihood for those who live on its upper slopes, and has been for a long time. The Roman emperors Nero and Hadrian both made the trip to the summit, and a monumental tower was even built on a hill ½ mile (1 km) to the south of the summit to commemorate Hadrian's ascent. The foundations of this tower were still to be seen when it became fashionable in the eighteenth century to ascend Etna as part of the Grand Tour of the Continent. Unfortunately, this historic site was lost when a restaurant was built there in the 1950s.

Etna also has some claim to be the cradle of volcanology, for Empedocles, a Greek philosopher now celebrated as the first known volcanologist, spent a good deal of time climbing the crater and studying its

Mount Erebus, Antarctica, is the most recently discovered of the volcanoes which are continuously active today.

activity around 400 BC. Legend has it that he died by falling into the crater, either by accident or possibly in a deliberate attempt to prove he was a god. The accessibility of Etna and its continuous activity mean that it is still a prime object of study, not just by volcanologists from Sicily and Italy, but also from Britain, France, Germany and the rest of Europe.

MOUNT EREBUS, ANTARCTICA

In contrast to Etna, Mount Erebus has one of the shortest observational records of its activity, being discovered by Sir James Ross in 1841. Even then, it was observed only intermittently by polar expeditions to the region, and was not climbed until a party from Shackleton's expedition made it to the top in March 1908. They found a series of older craters and calderas, and an active cone from which fume permanently issued. Standing on the edge when the mist cleared, they could see three active vents from which clouds of hissing vapour were loudly emitted. Every so often a dull boom could be heard, signalling a strombolian explosion, which turned the white vapour grey. They also found that fumaroles on Erebus consisted of spectacularly shaped ice towers, as the vapour from them immediately froze at the edge, building up funnels and chimneys akin to hornitos or geyser mounds.

A party from Scott's ill-fated expedition also climbed Erebus in December 1912 and found the activity to be similar, except that after leaving the crater, one of the party was caught in a much bigger explosion which threw blocks well outside the crater and scattered ash and Pélé's hair (see p. 77).

Regular observation of Erebus has only really begun in the last twenty years, but these recent observations, coupled with reports from earlier expeditions and the fact that Erebus was in eruption when first discovered in 1841 and always has a strong vapour plume, suggest that it has been a continuously active volcano since its discovery. In recent years Erebus has had an active molten lava lake at the bottom of the main crater and occasional Strombolian explosions.

Volcanologists working near an active vent on Mount Etna, Sicily.

Crater Lake, Oregon, with Wizard Island in the centre.

The blue waters of Oskuvatn lake, inside the Askja caldera, Iceland, with the crater Víti in the foreground.

12 VOLCANO SCENERY

CRATER LAKES

Volcanic craters are topographic depressions, so it is not surprising that they often fill with water to make lakes. However, such lakes are not as common as may be supposed, for volcanic cinders, ash and lava are usually highly porous, particularly if they have been fractured by ground movements. The water table at Mount Etna, for example, probably lies at least 3300 ft (1000 metres) below the summit, so no such lakes are found. However, where impervious or frozen layers occur within a volcano and crater lakes form, they can cause severe problems when the crater erupts. Either the water may become trapped and produce devastating phreatic explosions, or worse still, the water could be displaced and flood downhill to cause lahars.

Phreatic or phreatomagmatic explosions at crater lakes after a long, dormant period are typified by the final activity of the Chaîne des Puys, France, around 4000 BC. The last known event was also one of the largest, when a massive phreatomagmatic explosion came from Lac Pavin, now a calm lake in a wooded area. A similar eruption in Alaska in spring 1977 came from two such crater lakes – the Ukinrek maars – in a week or so of phreatomagmatic activity.

The displacement of crater lakes to produce floods and lahars has been all too evident in the disasters of this type that have occurred around the world. It was a lahar caused by drainage of the lake near the summit of Mount Pelée that caused the death of thirty workmen just before the destruction of St Pierre by nuées ardentes in 1902 (see p. 15). A similar event happened at Ruapehu volcano, New Zealand, in 1953, and the events at Ruiz volcano, Colombia, in 1985 have already been described on page 122. Kelut volcano, Indonesia, periodically ejects its crater lake during eruptions to form lahars which, in 1919 and 1966, took thousands of lives. Attempts to control the situation are described later (see p. 162).

Strangely enough, it has been suggested that the crater lake at Poás, Costa Rica, is responsible for calming down the volcano and keeping activity on an even keel. The lake varies considerably in volume throughout the year, falling to its lowest levels during the dry season. The temperature of the lake also varies, though it is usually within the range 40–70°C. During the last eruption in 1953 the lake disappeared altogether as rising temperatures within the crater caused it to evaporate, and an eruption followed. Since then there have been no eruptions, but the presence of the crater lake may be acting as a kind of heat buffer, absorbing and slowly dissipating the energy from the magma beneath and thus actually preventing eruptions.

Despite this lack of eruptive activity, Poás nevertheless provides spectacular geysering displays from time to time, as water on the floor of the lake becomes superheated due to trapping or hydrostatic pressure. When the trapped body of water rises and suddenly boils at once, a column of hot water, mud and ash rises from the steam clouds that envelop the lake in a fountain that may be tens or hundreds of feet high and plays for a few seconds before falling. In 1977 such a fountain ½ mile (1 km) high was observed; it fell on the flanks of the volcano and covered a large area with mud. In 1910 an extraordinary geyser 2½ miles (4 km) high was reported. Geysering through crater lakes has also occurred in recent years at both Ruapehu and White Island volcanoes in New Zealand, and at Karkar volcano off the coast of New Guinea.

Calderas may also fill with water in the same way as smaller crater lakes. Perhaps the best known example of a lake-filled caldera is Crater Lake, Oregon, a nearly circular lake 6 miles (10 km) across surrounded by the cliffs of the caldera wall which are 2000 ft (600 metres) high in places. A cinder cone called Wizard Island rises from the lake and the spectacular scenery has meant that Crater Lake, now a national park, is visited by thousands of tourists every year. Similar but bigger volcanic depressions filled with lakes are also found: Lake Taupo in New Zealand is 18½ miles (30 km) in diameter, while Lake Toba in Sumatra measures 18½ x 50 miles (30 x 80 km), probably the largest volcanic depression on Earth, consisting of a vast, irregular caldera. Irregularly shaped calderas of this size are sometimes called *volcano-tectonic depressions.*

OLD VOLCANOES

Volcanic rocks cover a great deal of the Earth's surface, including most of the sea floors, and even in areas that have had no volcanoes for tens of millions of years,

OVERLEAF: *Spectacular geysering from the sulphurous lake of Poás volcano, Costa Rica, attracts many visitors.*

PREVIOUS PAGE: The Giant's Causeway in County Antrim, Northern Ireland, is the eroded remains of a 50-million-year-old lava flow, with pillars created by the cooling joints.

such as Great Britain, there are thousands of examples of old volcanoes and volcanic rocks to be found. If we restrict ourselves to old volcanoes that have been active within the last 10,000 years, there are still a surprising number in unexpected places. For example, there are dozens in China and the Himalayas, Turkey and the Middle East, a couple in eastern Australia and even in northwest Europe. Many of these more recent old volcanoes are preserved virtually intact, as at the Chaîne des Puys in the Massif Central of France, where around 100 craters, cones and domes are now concealed by vegetation. (The last eruption in the Chaîne des Puys was about 5000 years ago.)

As well as these French volcanoes, Europe in the past 10,000 years has had explosive maars erupting in the Eifel district of Germany, other eruptions in northern Spain and Greece, and of course many in Italy, quite apart from the presently active Vesuvius, Etna and Aeolian volcanoes. Most of these have the potential to become active at any time in the future.

The western United States, excluding Alaska and Hawaii, has well-known volcanoes that have been active in historic time, such as Mount St Helens, Lassen Peak and Mount Shasta, but it also has over sixty volcanoes that have been active in the past 10,000 years, mostly in the Cascades and the Sierra Nevada, with some in the Rockies as well. Following the Mount St Helens eruption of 1980, these have been particularly studied because of potential future eruptions. Many, such as Sunset Crater, Arizona, look

Ship Rock, New Mexico, is a beautiful example of the volcanic neck of an old volcano, laid bare by erosion.

virtually the same as when they last erupted, with beautiful pyroclastic cones and fresh-looking lava flows. Further back in time, within the last million years, there have been some very big eruptions in the western United States at Yellowstone, Valles and Long Valley calderas. In fact, the last-named is now being watched with concern following an increase in earthquakes there in 1982, together with uplift and an increase in fumarolic activity. Past eruptions from Long Valley include one 700,000 years ago that formed an ignimbrite that devastated several hundred square miles. Such an eruption today would cause widespread destruction and loss of life on an unthinkable scale.

Older volcanoes are even more widespread. Vast tracts of the eastern USA, the eastern countries of South America, southern Africa, North Africa, Australia, Antarctica, Europe, Central Asia and India, which have little or no present-day volcanism, are covered by volcanoes or volcanic rocks that date from thousands of millions to tens of millions of years ago. Most remnants of these old volcanoes are dissected by erosion and bear no resemblance to the original shape of the volcano, but the interior rocks and structure are exposed, which can reveal a great deal about what kind of volcano it was and how it erupted. Such remnants may, none the less, be spectacular. Ship Rock, New Mexico, for example, is an eroded volcanic neck with wall-like dykes radiating from it.

To illustrate the different phases of volcanism that may occur to a small area of the world with no volcanoes today, we may look at the geological history of Britain. In common with other parts of the Earth's surface, Britain has been moving around on a continental plate for hundreds of millions of years. The configuration and movement of these plates has been constantly changing, and a study of past climates and magnetic directions seems to indicate that about 600 million years ago Britain was in the southern hemisphere a long way south of the Equator. It gradually moved to Equatorial regions between 400 and 250 million years ago, moving steadily north to its present position since then. During its wanderings, it occasionally found itself near spreading axes, subduction zones or other places conducive to volcanic activity. The earliest volcanic rocks found in Britain (from the Midlands) are 1000 million years old, but apart from these earlier times, Britain has undergone four more recent periods of volcanic activity which have had a profound effect on the landscape.

Some 450 million years ago most of Britain was under water, but North Wales was the site of intense volcanic activity and huge volcanoes grew out of the sea to form volcanic islands. Widespread ignimbrites characterized the activity in this region and some of these can be traced for distances of over 18 miles (30 km), from Snowdonia up to the north coast of Wales. These repeated eruptions must have been similar to that of Krakatoa in 1883 (see pp 9–11), some of them on a much bigger scale.

Around 400 million years ago another great period of volcanic activity in Britain produced further volcanoes whose lavas and pyroclastics can now be found in Glen Coe, Ben Nevis and the Ochil Hills in the Highlands of Scotland, and also in the Cheviot Hills on the Scottish border. Among the best-known volcanic features from this period is a 360-million-year-old caldera in Glen Coe which measures 5 x 9 miles (8 x 14 km).

During the Carboniferous period, around 300 million years ago, volcanism affected much of Britain, including Devon and Cornwall. Basalt lavas were erupted in the Pennines, and the Whin Sill in Northumberland was also intruded during this period. At the same time a small group of volcanic vents in Edinburgh were active, including a composite volcanic neck with two vents, which came to be known as Arthur's Seat, and Castle Rock, upon which Edinburgh Castle now stands.

During the building of the Alps, about 70 million years ago, there was widespread eruption of fluid basaltic lavas from long cracks and fissures, similar to volcanism in Iceland today. The largest of these is in Antrim, Northern Ireland, and covers more than 1550 square miles (4000 square km). The tendency of basalt to form cooling cracks, which produce polygonal columns or *columnar jointing* stacked at right angles to the surface, has produced some beautiful landforms in Scotland – at Fingal's Cave on the island of Staffa, and off the Isle of Mull – and at the Giant's Causeway on the north coast of Antrim.

Could volcanoes ever become active again in Britain? The country's last volcano ceased erupting about 50 million years ago, but in view of the wanderings of the continents and the repeated episodes of volcanism over the last few hundred million years, Britain must expect further phases of volcanic activity in the future. However, to generate the magma necessary for volcanism, changes in the tectonic structure are necessary that are not going to happen in the near future, so it is extremely unlikely that volcanoes will start erupting again in Britain during the next few million years.

13
INVESTIGATING VOLCANOES

GEOLOGICAL MAPPING OF VOLCANOES

Until recently, the geological mapping and analysis of rocks from old volcanoes were the only means whereby the structure and workings of a volcano could be studied. Although numerous other methods of study have now been developed, geological mapping remains the most widely used technique for understanding volcanoes in general.

Once stream valleys or other types of erosion have eaten into a volcano, the insides are exposed and can be studied at leisure. In fact, many such dissected volcanoes are found in countries which are now far from any centres of volcanic activity. The many old volcanoes in England, Wales, Scotland and Northern Ireland described in the previous section, and the intensive studies carried out on these ancient structures, meant that British geologists became world leaders in volcanology at the turn of the century. Geological study and mapping are now carried out at active and inactive volcanoes the world over to provide vital information on past eruptive behaviour and its lessons for the future.

The sequence of activity in an old volcano can be deduced from the type and thickness of the exposed strata. Each eruption will have left its layer of lava, or ash, or pyroclastic flow deposit, and the thickness of these layers will indicate their relative importance. A long series of lavas followed by a long series of explosive pyroclastic eruptions indicates a change in a volcano's eruptive behaviour, and a long period of dormancy between eruptions will show up in the geological sequence as a soil horizon on top of one layer, later overlain by another. An even longer period of dormancy may show up as an eroded surface in some places. This means that erosion has eaten into a layer or layers before they were covered up by further eruptions.

In addition, sections through volcanoes will reveal the volcanic chimneys and pipes up which the magma rose to the surface, together with the dykes, sills, laccoliths and magma chambers in which it was stored before eruption or before it solidified underground. All these magmas can be sampled and their mineralogy used to provide evidence of how long they have spent in a given chamber and how far beneath the surface. The individual lavas of the sequence within the volcanic edifice can also be analysed to look for minerals and trace elements which might give clues to the depths at which they were stored and the length of time they spent there.

The sequence of activity derived from the superposition of the various lava and pyroclastic layers within the volcano itself will become much more precise if dates can be assigned to one or more layers. It was not until 1959 that isotopic dating was used in geology – on an old lava flow in central France. Since that time such dating has become a widespread tool in volcanology. The method relies on the fact that, over a period of time, some isotopes decay into more stable ones; therefore, the higher the proportion of unstable isotope, the younger the age of the sample. For carbon dating, which is applicable to fairly recent deposits, it is necessary to find the remains of plant or animal life, such as charred wood beneath a lava flow, or within a pyroclastic flow or ashfall. Where an ashfall forms a layer within a soil or peat deposit, organic matter in the soil or peat just above and below the layer can be dated to set limits on the age of the ash layer.

Isotopic dating methods have gradually improved over the years and it is now possible to date events up to 50,000 years old using carbon 14, while other isotopic methods, such as potassium/argon and uranium/thorium dating, may be used for earlier ages. More recently, thermoluminescence, originally used in archaeology for dating baked quartz grains in ceramics, has been successfully adapted for measuring the age of quartz grains warmed by volcanic flows or included in bombs (see p. 44). This means that the flows themselves, rather than material included or adjacent to them, can be specifically dated.

These methods mean that, theoretically at least, the sequences of activity in a volcano or a volcanic region can be dated over hundreds of thousands of years. In addition, the relative positions, chemistry and mineralogy of the erupted lavas, ashes and pyroclastic flows, together with the subsurface configuration and composition of the various magma storage areas, can be used to show where the magmas that produced the eruptions came from, at what levels they were stored and for how long.

Geological mapping and sampling of a volcano helps to decipher its past history.

Geophysical techniques such as magnetometry provide important information on what is happening beneath the visible surface of the volcano.

Unfortunately, in practice this can never be done for a single volcano. The vagaries of erosion mean that the part of the volcano you want to see is rarely exposed at the surface, and even if one part of a volcano is well exposed – a magma chamber, for example – then other parts, such as the surface sequence of lava flows, are likely to have been entirely removed by erosion. Nevertheless, the increasing geological knowledge of thousands of past volcanoes and volcanic products the world over has built up, and is continuing to build up, an extremely useful general knowledge on the workings of volcanoes.

GEOLOGY ON ACTIVE VOLCANOES

The same techniques of geological mapping and dating can also be applied to active volcanoes, particularly large, persistently active ones. These may be hundreds of thousands of years old and their slopes may already be dissected by erosion, allowing their past history to be unravelled and perhaps giving clues to their future behaviour. Many of the techniques for dating lava flows, ashfalls and pyroclastic flows (described in the previous section) can be better applied to active volcanoes, as they are younger and therefore give more accurate results. Very recent flows on active volcanoes can also be dated quite accurately by determining the direction of remanent magnetization provided the wandering of the magnetic pole is well known for the period required.

Although geological investigations can never be used to predict precise times and positions of eruptions, a great deal of information about the recent interior workings of the volcano and the movement of magma within it in the immediate past can nevertheless be gleaned from regular sampling of the lavas or the pyroclastic material that is thrown out. Magma is generated at depths below 30 miles (50 km) by partial melting of the upper mantle. A number of things may happen between its formation deep down and its appearance at the surface and there may be many stages in its ascent; for example, it may be temporarily stored in an unknown number of deep or near-surface magma chambers and it may remain an unknown time in each storage area. However, each time it pauses in its ascent, processes will come into play which will leave evidence of its progress.

The most obvious of these processes is differentiation (see p. 87). Magmas gradually become more differentiated the longer they spend stored in a particular chamber, as lighter components float to the top and heavier ones sink to the bottom. This differentiation may show up in the lavas erupted from a volcano during the course of a single eruption. If the magma has been stored in a chamber or dyke, the lavas may slowly change their composition from the beginning to the end of the eruption. First, the top of the storage area is erupted, enriched in the lighter components and depleted in the heavier ones; then the lower parts of the storage area are erupted, depleted in the lighter constituents and enriched in the heavier ones. A lava that does not change composition in this way suggests that it has not been stored for any length of time.

Alternatively, if no new magma is coming into the chamber from below, and if only a small part of the magma chamber is extruded in each eruption, the compositon of the sampled lavas may slowly change from one eruption to the next. As lower parts of the magma chamber are emptied, the lavas will become steadily more evolved over several eruptions as the same magma continues to differentiate with time. If magma is being supplied more or less constantly to the chamber from beneath, the magma is kept on the move and differentiation is limited, though in these circumstances some differentiation may take place in a dyke or other offshoot from the main storage area where the magma can remain undisturbed. If magma is injected into a storage area intermittently in successive batches, the newly arrived primary magma will mix with the magma already in the chamber which has started to differentiate, creating a complex mixture.

Successive batches of magma rising from below the magma chamber may also have slightly different compositions, which will further complicate the situation. Magmas may also be complicated by stoping, as xenoliths falling from the roof or sides of the chamber are incorporated into it (see p. 86). If the magma has forced its way through sedimentary rocks, these xenoliths may have very different chemical compositions from the primary magma and alter its bulk composition. This happens particularly at subduction zones where magma rises through continental crust and sediments. Detailed study of the minerals and crystals found in a lava may also indicate under what pressure they were formed and therefore at what depth beneath the surface.

In theory all these details on magma storage and history could be deduced by sampling lavas from successive eruptions of a volcano, either directly as they erupt, or in sections through long sequences of erupted products where stratified layers are exposed and can be dated isotopically or otherwise. In practice, of course, problems arise both in the interpretation of compositional changes and the availability of lavas for sampling. Nevertheless, *cycles of activity* have been observed at many volcanoes, either from historically known eruptions or from sequences of different compositions or eruptive styles in the geological record.

For some volcanoes, such as Mount Etna, Vesuvius, Kilauea, Kelut and Colima, cycle lengths based on average repose periods, or times between particularly large eruptions, have been determined as 7, 15, 11.1, 13 and about 100 years respectively. Unfortunately, these cycles seem to be temporary features, often very variable in length (the supposed Vesuvius cycle varies from 5 to 25 years). Apart from some exceptions which could well be fortuitous, attempts to predict future eruptions of these volcanoes on the basis of their cycles have been disastrous. Vesuvius, for example, ceased erupting altogether in 1944, underlining the fact that, although regular eruptive behaviour may last for a brief period while the determining influences remain stable, small changes in these influences can disrupt cyclic activity, making the periods so variable that, like the weather, a great many observations have to be continuously carried out to predict accurately what will happen.

14
MONITORING AND PREDICTING ACTIVE VOLCANOES

SEISMIC STUDIES

Seismic monitoring, or the recording of earthquakes, including those far too small to be felt, is the mainstay of eruption prediction. Most of the major eruptions for which there is sufficient information, including the terrible eruptions of Vesuvius in AD 79, Mount Katmai in 1912, Mount Lamington in 1951, Bezymianny in 1956 and Ruiz in 1985, were all preceded by earthquakes for at least a few days, in most cases strong enough to be felt without the aid of a seismometer.

Before magma reaches the surface to start an eruption, it has to shoulder aside the rocks to get there, so an eruption is virtually always accompanied by seismic activity of some sort. The earthquakes can be recorded by a *seismometer*, an instrument which, in its most widely used design, records the time and intensity of an earthquake by tracing the ground motion on a revolving drum. More modern designs record the signals electronically and store them on tape or, better still, transmit them directly by radio or satellite link to a centre remote from the volcano, where they can be stored or traced by a *seismograph* (a revolving drum on a seismometer) for immediate scrutiny.

Earthquakes associated with volcanic activity may be quite small, particularly in basaltic volcanoes, and may be detectable in only one particular region of the volcano. It is therefore necessary to have a network of several seismometers spread over the volcano so that each earthquake can be recorded by at least two, and preferably three, instruments, allowing the position, magnitude and depth of the earthquake to be accurately determined. The more closely spaced the seismometers, the more accurate the calculations.

In some eruptions earthquakes begin deep beneath the volcano and then occur, at progressively shallower depths as the magma rises to the surface. In other eruptions this pattern does not occur, as deep earthquakes may cause movements at all levels within the volcano. The most reliable sign of an impending eruption is the rapid increase in the number of shallow earthquakes, and in some cases the rate of increase can be used to predict the time of eruption. These earthquakes are distinct events caused by the fracturing of rocks as magma forces its way to the surface.

Shallow earthquakes are quite distinct from *harmonic tremor*, also known as *volcanic tremor*, when the ground

Seismometers provide the best immediate warning of an imminent eruption.

trembles continuously. This tremor accompanies most eruptions and is caused by the magma rushing through the conduit and causing the volcano to vibrate at a particular frequency. The frequency will depend upon the shape of the conduit through which the magma passes. Harmonic tremor is usually a very local phenomenon, detectable only by sensitive instruments close to the vent, but in exceptional cases it has been felt without a seismometer over a distance of several miles.

Although seismic information has been used successfully to predict volcanic activity many times in the past, it should be emphasized that no single method can be relied upon to predict eruptions accurately. This fact was emphatically proved by the events at La Soufrière volcano, Guadaloupe, in 1976. Earthquakes steadily increased from November 1975, when twenty-five were recorded, until March 1976, when nearly 700 occurred, about 200 of them strong enough to be felt by those living on the volcano.

Since seismic crises are common on volcanoes of this type, not much notice was taken, though nothing so strong had occurred for fifteen years. However, on 8 July there was a strong explosion and ash eruption which plunged the volcano into darkness for forty minutes, and others occurred on 25 July and 9 August. These were assumed to be purely phreatic explosions, but after a further one on 12 August it was decided to evacuate the 72,000 people living near the volcano. When the number of earthquakes increased from 700 per month to 900 per day on 17 August, it looked as if a major eruption must occur, but it never came. The costly evacuation had been unnecessary and caused great controversy in the months that followed. However, one positive aspect of this crisis was that the government increased its funding of volcanology so that similar fiascos could be avoided in the future.

GROUND DEFORMATION

Ground deformation is second only to seismicity in eruption prediction, and taken together the two techniques provide the most useful information about what is happening inside a volcano. The term 'ground deformation' is applied to the slow creep of the ground surface in response to changes within the volcano. Different volcanoes respond in different ways, but in the simplest cases a slowly filling magma chamber a few miles beneath the volcano will exert increasing pressure which will cause the volcano to swell at the surface, sometimes by more than 3 ft (1 metre). As long as magma continues to fill the chamber, this *inflation* will continue, until finally the pressure exceeds the material strength of the chamber roof, the rocks rupture and the magma rushes through the cracks to erupt. Once the pressure is relieved and the magma chamber empties, the volcano deflates rapidly until the eruption ends. If the volcano has a regular supply of magma coming into the chamber, as at Kilauea in Hawaii, inflation will immediately start again and continue until the next eruption.

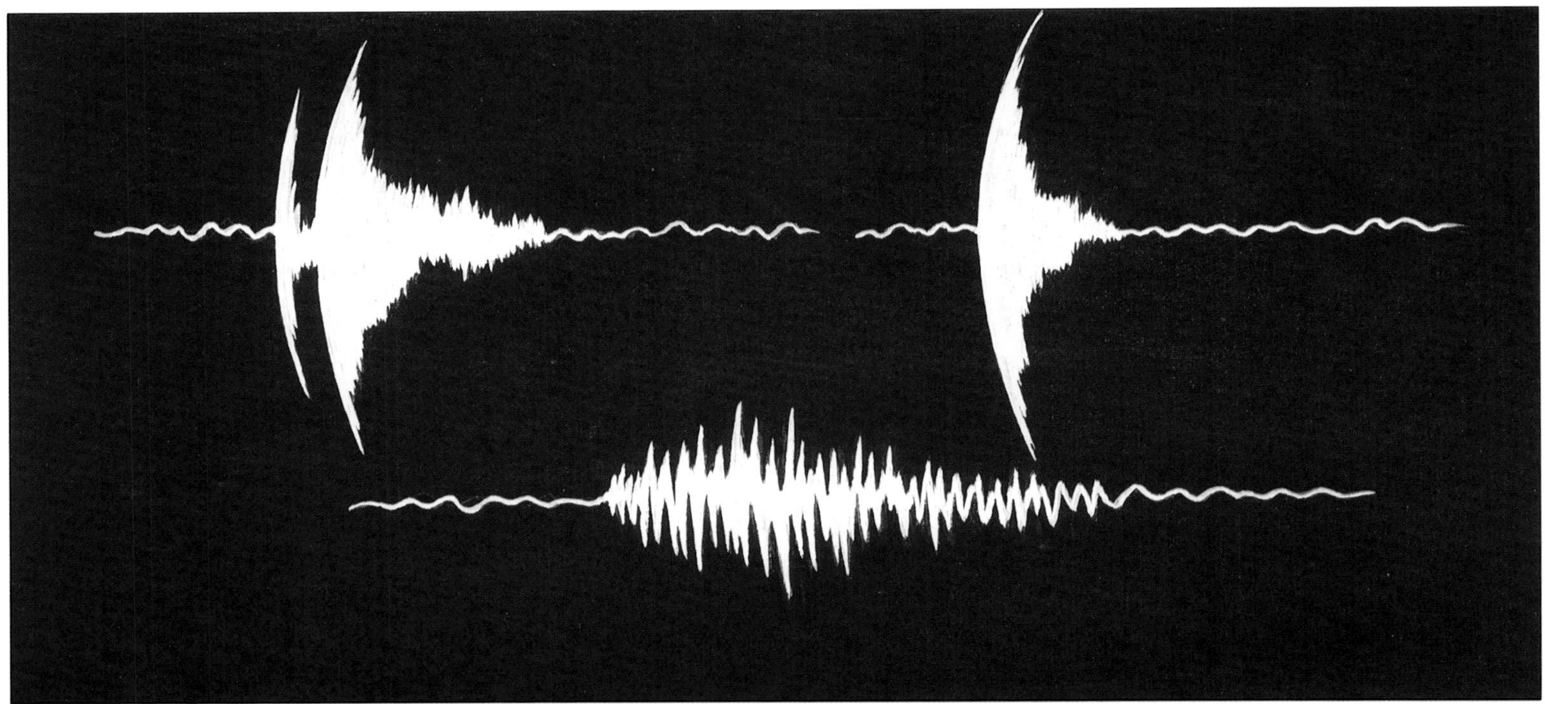

Different types of earthquake produce different traces on the seismograph. Traces of far (top left), near (top right) and long period (bottom) earthquakes are commonly recorded before and during eruptions.

These ground movements are measured by standard surveying techniques in which the heights and positions of markers are regularly determined with great accuracy so that the position and amount of inflation can be followed from year to year. This gives useful information on where the eruption is likely to occur, but to get a better estimate of when the eruption will take place, continuously recording *tilt meters* are used. These are extremely sensitive instruments, which can detect changes in the slope of the ground to a millionth of a degree. As the volcano inflates, the tilt meters on its flanks will tilt further and further away from the summit, but as soon as deflation occurs at the start of the eruption, they will rapidly tilt back towards the summit. This information can be transmitted back to the volcano observatory at regular intervals.

Kilauea has very shallow slopes of only a few degrees, and the same pattern of balloon-like inflation occurs at other flat volcanoes such as Sakurajima, Japan, where it was discovered in 1914, Krafla in Iceland, and Pozzuoli in the Bay of Naples. However, on Etna the situation is very different. It is a high, steep-sided volcano, there are no signs of a shallow magma chamber and the magma is not confined but free to rise up and down the central pipe as it likes. As a result, the ground deformation is much smaller, while the steepness may cause the top of the mountain to subside under its own weight and the flanks to swell before an eruption, as happened in 1983. Another tall, steep-sided volcano – Mount St Helens – also showed subsidence at the summit and swelling on its northern flank before the 1980 eruption, but on a massive scale (see p. 118).

Ground deformation is also a useful technique for exploring inside a volcano. The shape and size of the swelling before an eruption can give information on the depth of the magma chamber. A broad, low swelling indicates a deep magma chamber while a narrow swelling indicates a shallow chamber; the depth can be calculated from the movement of markers at a number of stations. Where a dyke has been intruded underground, a distinct pattern of displacement occurs at the surface, with the ground subsiding over the dyke itself, often by more than 3 ft (1 metre), and swelling on either side. Again, the depth of the dyke can be calculated from the distance between the two parallel swellings, and the dip angle of the dyke from the relative size of the two swellings.

Regular surveying and distance measurement between markers can also reveal a great deal about tectonic movements associated with the volcano and the way these affect activity. The spreading Mid-Atlantic Ridge can be monitored in Iceland by taking regular measurements across the axis, while in Japan a series of stations has recently been set up to look at movements around a series of volcanoes over the subduction zone there. This project is using the Global Positioning System (GPS), a new technique which uses signals from a series of satellites to establish the positions of widely spaced points more rapidly than with conventional surveying methods.

OTHER METHODS OF PREDICTION

Gravity measurements

If you weigh an apple with a spring balance, then climb a mountain and weigh it again, the apple will weigh slightly less at the summit than at the bottom. This is because you are further away from the centre of the Earth at the top of the mountain, so the force of gravity, which pulls the apple downwards and stretches the spring, is slightly less.

If you are on a volcano and weigh the apple while standing on a thick deposit of low-density pumice and ash, then move to a point at the same height, but on top of a thick layer of dense lava, the apple will weigh slightly more over the lava because the greater density of the lava adds a tiny amount to the gravitational attraction at that point.

The differences in gravitational attraction are minute, however, and to measure them a *gravimeter* is used. This consists of an extremely sensitive spring balance which is kept at a constant temperature inside a carefully insulated chamber and has to be very precisely levelled. This instrument can measure height changes as the ground swells up before an eruption but, more importantly, when used in conjunction with accurate surveying, it can be used as a densitometer to detect changes in density below the ground as magma moves around inside the volcano before eruption. Even if the volcano has an open system so that no inflation occurs before eruption, the increase in density over a magma storage area as it fills up can be detected with a gravimeter.

Gas emission

As magma nears the surface before eruption, the confining pressure decreases and it starts to bubble and lose gas. This gas can often be seen as it causes emission of *fume* (a general term meaning gas, vapour

Ground deformation indicates where and when an eruption will take place.
TOP: *A surveyor measures the inflation of the ground as magma pushes it up before an eruption.*
MIDDLE: *The inflation continues until the moment the eruption begins.*
BOTTOM: *The release of pressure when the eruption starts allows the ground to drop back to its original position.*

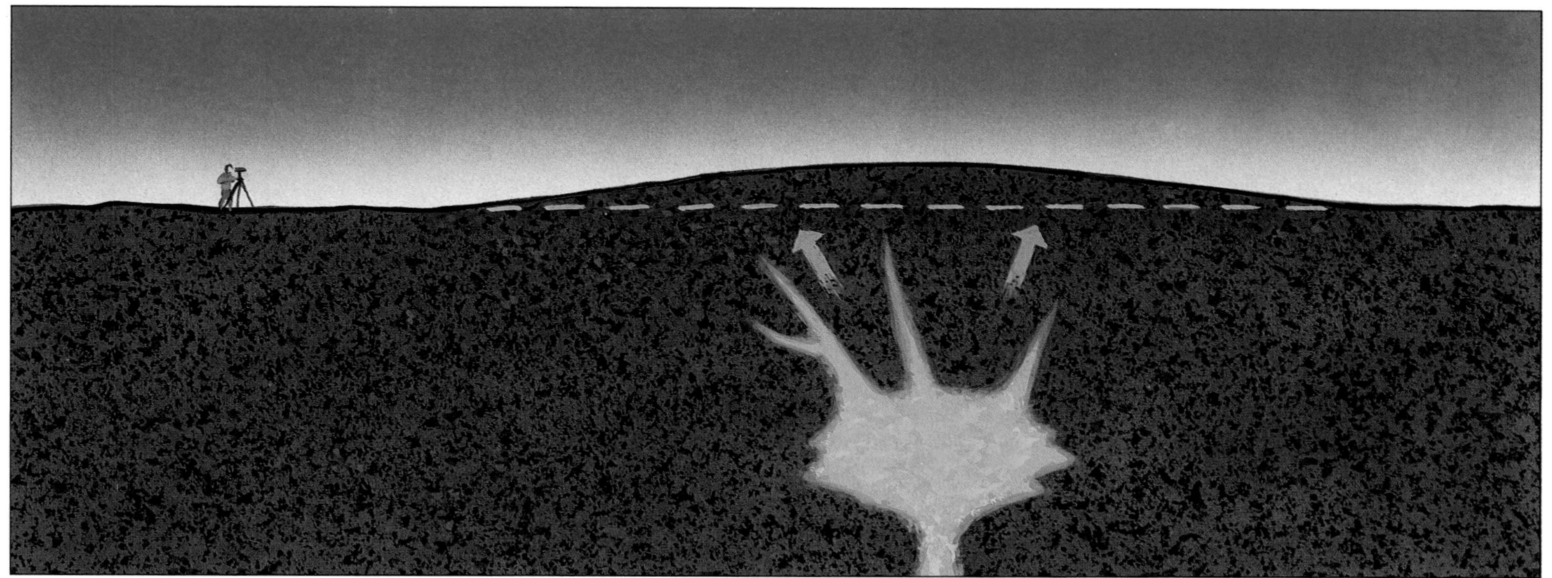

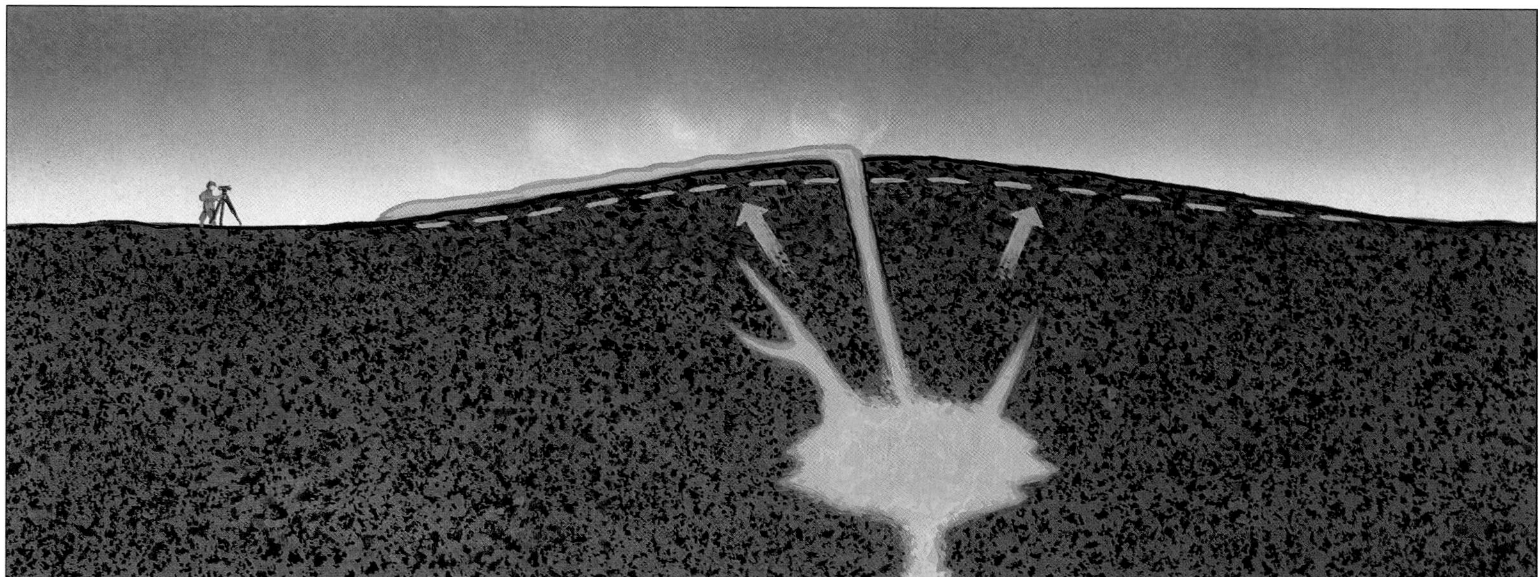

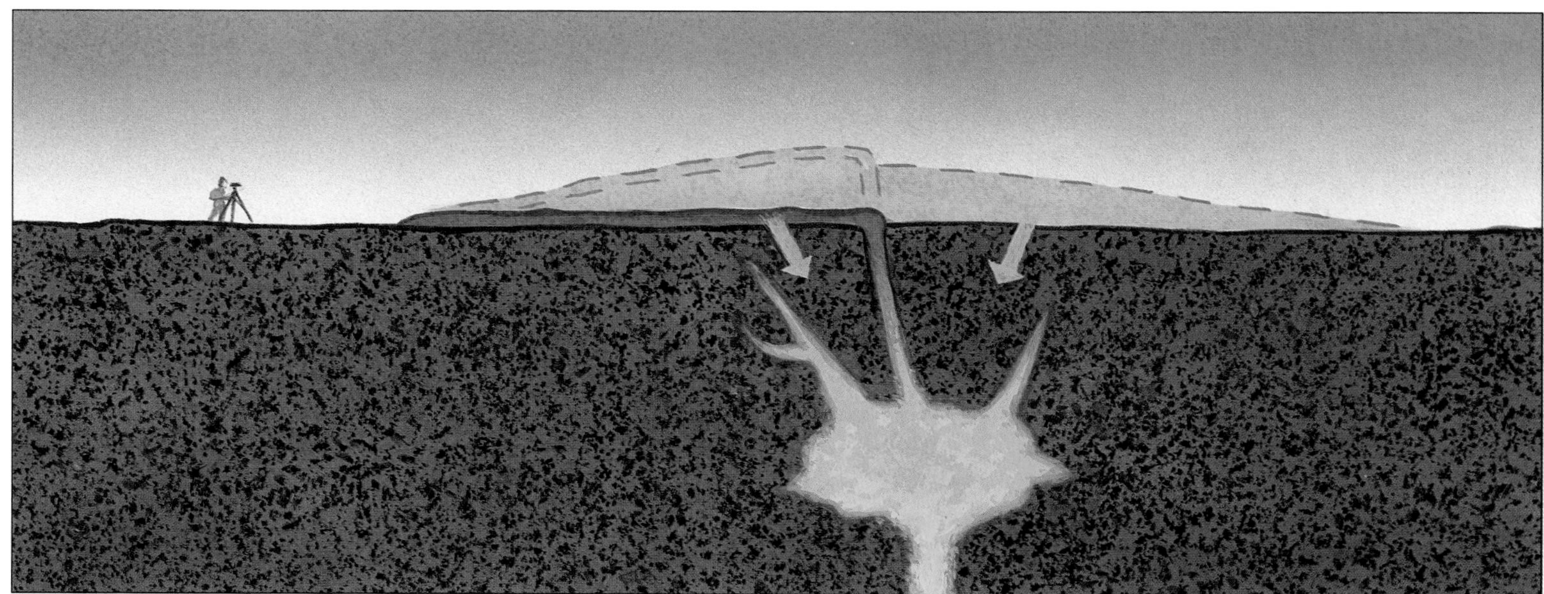

Measuring ground movements with distance meter and theodolite near the summit of Mount Etna, Sicily.

Temperature, gas and gravity measurements are all used to detect how magma is moving beneath the volcano and how near the surface it lies. This helps to find out how the volcano functions and is important in eruption prediction and in determining how large an eruption will be.

OVERLEAF: *A French team flying over Raung volcano, Indonesia, in a microlight aircraft (motorized hang-glider). This gives cheap and rapid access to otherwise inaccessible volcanoes.*

and solid particles which look like smoke but are not) at the summit crater, but it may also permeate through the ground in minute quantities all over the volcano. Pronounced increases in the emission rate of these gases indicates that the magma is nearing the surface and that an eruption is therefore likely to occur. These increases can be measured with detectors left in place either at the summit crater where the emission rate is high or, with sensitive apparatus, by detectors placed in the ground far from the summit. The latter have to be more sensitive, but where permanently installed, they have the advantage that they are more likely to survive the eruption. The measurements can be transmitted back by radio or satellite link on a regular basis.

Apart from the rate of gas emission, the composition of the gas may change as an eruption draws near, so sampling apparatus capable of detecting different gases and their relative quantities can also be installed. Alternatively, these measurements can be carried out by *lidar*, a technique analogous to radar but using light instead of radio waves. A laser beam using light of different wavelengths is passed through the plume and reflections give information on the height, composition and number of dust particles or molecules of gas. The disadvantage of lidar is that it requires a clear sky to make measurements.

Temperature measurements

These are simple to make and may be useful indicators of impending activity as the ground heats up before an eruption. Recently, infra-red measurements from satellites have greatly increased the possibilities of measuring temperature at a large number of very remote volcanoes. Potentially, this could be an extremely useful source of information, but there are some problems involved, as soil and surface type, rainfall, snow, seasonal changes in vegetation cover and differential surface heating by sunlight can all produce considerable changes in measured temperature.

Magnetic measurements

These have not been widely used, but at some volcanoes may be extremely useful. As rocks heat up, they gradually lose their magnetic attraction, so before an eruption the magnetic field around a volcano may change as the magma invades shallow reservoirs.

Electrical measurements

These have also been used to investigate subsurface structure and heat sources within a volcano. In particular, self-potential measurements have proved useful in identifying bodies of magma beneath the surface. Tiny electric charges naturally occur at certain places on the volcano, apparently set up by water circulation over submerged heat sources, and measurement of these currents at different locations on the volcano gives information on the position and evolution of these hot bodies of magma.

VOLCANO SURVEILLANCE

All the instrumentation described in the previous sections can be set up as continuously recording installations, with the data from a number of stations scattered over the volcano transmitted by radio or satellite link to a volcano observatory or other remote station. Many such observatories have been set up at volcanoes the world over, with perhaps the best financed and best run being the Hawaiian volcano observatory at Kilauea, and the recently established observatory at Piton de la Fournaise volcano, on Réunion Island in the Indian Ocean.

Both observatories have a permanently installed network of seismic stations and tilt meters, both of which run continuously. Data from these stations is transmitted to the observatory, where events can be followed as they happen. These two techniques give the first warning that activity is increasing, but to confirm this and to obtain more details both observatories have a large ground deformation network of points that can be surveyed to see how the entire volcano is changing. In addition, gas sampling and temperature, gravity and electrical measurements are regularly made to give further clues to what is happening. At both volcanoes, eruptions can fairly successfully be predicted from a few days to a few hours before they happen, in time for local authorities and rescue services to be alerted, and any necessary evacuation carried out. However, many countries simply cannot afford even the modest expense of such systems, but even they can keep an eye on volcanoes through periodic visits by volcanologists.

Where accessibility to volcanoes is difficult, as in Indonesia, a microlight aircraft (motorized hang glider) can be used. This has the advantages of being cheap to run and being able to land and take off in very small spaces, such as crater floors, allowing the volcanologists to take quick and regular measurements at each volcano. Several potentially dangerous volcanoes can be visited per day in this way.

The SPOT 1 satellite over the Galapagos Islands in the eastern Pacific.

N5238R

Evacuation and rescue operations require a sophisticated degree of planning and a well-funded and organized civil protection service.

PUBLIC WARNING AND EVACUATION

Perhaps the most difficult task a volcanologist has to face is the vexed question of civil protection from the lethal effects of volcanoes. The main problem lies in the fact that there are only about half a dozen volcanoes in the world which have sufficient permanently installed instrumentation on them to predict their activity accurately. The result is that volcanologists at inadequately monitored sites are usually left guessing the likely outcome. Inevitably, there will be a variety of opinions, if not diametrically opposed views, if vital information is not available.

When should a threatened population be evacuated? There are a number of occasions when evacuation has been carried out and nothing has happened, as at Tristan da Cunha in 1962, La Soufrière de St Vincent in 1971 and La Soufrière de Guadaloupe in 1976. On the other hand, it is possible to cite many tragedies caused by not evacuating, the most renowned being at Ruiz volcano, Colombia, in 1985, and Mount Pelée, Martinique, in 1902. Professional opinion deems it better to err on the side of caution, but this is not always the view of the local population, who depend upon the land for their livelihood and cannot afford to lose too many days' work. Impatience with volcanologists and the civil authorities is not restricted to poor or underdeveloped nations; indeed, it is amply illustrated by a recent case in USA.

When the first steam and ash explosions began at Mount St Helens at the end of March 1980, the sixty people living nearby were evacuated (apart from one who refused to go), plus about 300 lumberjacks in temporary accommodation. The roads were then blocked by guards to prevent entry into the danger zone. After a month had passed with no increase in activity, those who derived their living from logging in the numerous forests on the volcano became extremely impatient as they sank deeper into financial difficulties. Many of them began to work clandestinely inside the danger zone, bypassing the guards by using little-known paths. When the catastrophic eruption of 18 May took place, most of the fifty-seven people killed inside the danger area were there because they had deliberately disobeyed warnings and were working without authorization.

Even when volcanologists are certain that a volcano will erupt, it is sometimes extremely difficult for the civil authorities to do anything about it. The city of Naples, for example, lies close to Vesuvius and there are also a number of other old volcanoes in and around the city and its suburbs. If the worst happened and an eruption from one of these old volcanoes produced an ignimbrite, devastation would threaten about 4 million people, together with thousands of factories and businesses. In this instance, it is doubtful whether a complete evacuation of such a large number of people living in such a small area could be effected in the time available. The problem was highlighted recently when the ground rose by 9 ft (3 metres) (see p. 89).

In situations where evacuation cannot take place rapidly enough, or where financial considerations make it impracticable, there is still a lot that can be done to mitigate the effects of highly explosive eruptions and pyroclastic flows, particularly near the edges of the devastated area. Advice to the population on what to do and what to wear, and even on the construction of shelters, might save a large number of lives. However, like the advice given on civil defence in the case of a nuclear attack, this is a risky and haphazard kind of protection and very much second best to full evacuation.

The problems of evacuation and civil protection have received a great deal of attention in Japan in recent years. Volcanoes such as Sakurajima, which threaten big eruptions, have led to the development of a rigorous evacuation procedure; just as fire drill practices take place elsewhere, volcano alerts are regularly held. Some Japanese volcanoes have also been the site of repeated lahars, which tend to occur in the same areas and follow the same valleys. Trip wires and electronic surveillance systems have now been set up at critical points across these valleys, which set off an alarm in the event of danger so that people further down the valley receive adequate forewarning.

Just how much can be done to save lives without sophisticated equipment by a poor nation on a limited budget was recently illustrated by the eruption of Mount Pinatubo in the Philippines. On 15/16 June 1991 one of the largest explosive eruptions this century ejected ash to an altitude of 20 miles (30 km) and generated a series of large pyroclastic flows. Despite this cataclysmic event, carefully timed evacuation was carried out from late April onwards, when the first signs of activity commenced, so that just before the final series of vast explosions, about 200,000 people had been evacuated from a zone extending to 25 miles (40 km) from the volcano. As a result, only 300 people were killed.

15 CONTROLLING VOLCANOES

CONTROL OF LAVA FLOWS

The first recorded attempt to stop damage by a lava flow was during the 1669 eruption of Etna (see p. 105). By breaking open the solidified crust at the edge of the flow, the hotter and more fluid lava inside poured out and began flowing away from the edge of the flow in a new direction. Strangely enough, there is no record of another attempt to divert a flow until 1935, when a lava flow from Mauna Loa volcano in Hawaii was threatening the town of Hilo. It had been suggested some years earlier that a lava flow might be diverted by bombing it at one of three critical places: the crater itself, where a new breach could be created to set the flow off in another direction; the sides of the flow, to destroy the containing levees and allow a new branch to flow, as at Mount Etna in 1669; or a lava tube high up the flow, which could be broken open to restart the flow again beside the natural one.

This last method was used in 1935, the idea being to bomb the flow as it progressed along a tunnel under ground in the hope that the debris from the explosion might block the tube. The lava would then escape from the breach and begin creating a new flow above ground, which would cut off the supply of lava to the flow front and stop it advancing. Eventually, of course, the new flow would reach a point where it again threatened property, so it would be bombed again. This strategy appeared to be at least partially successful. The main lava tube was bombed by aircraft, the tube was blocked by debris from the explosions and a new flow poured out of the hole blown in the roof of the tube. The lava front slowed, finally stopping six days later.

In 1942, when a similar eruption produced another flow towards Hilo, a second attempt at bombing was made. This time the levee of the main lava channel was bombed. The lava poured out, advancing alongside the original flow as planned, but unfortunately rejoined the original flow channel lower down.

A different method altogether was tried when the prehistoric volcano Helgafell, on the island of Vestmannaeyjar, Iceland, suddenly burst into life in 1973 (see p. 115). In view of the threat to the fishing industry, the government immediately made funds available for a serious attempt to limit the advance of the flow. It was decided to try and cool down the flow front by pouring water on it, thus slowing its progress, and to build barriers to control its course. At first city water supplies were used, but later it was decided to use a pump ship in the harbour.

It was quickly realized that a great deal more water was needed to slow the advance sufficiently, and eventually forty-seven pumps were used to spray a total of 35 cubic ft (1 cubic metre) of sea water per second on to the flow. Although priority was given to cooling the flow front, a system of pipes made it possible to cool the flow over a distance of ½ mile (1 km). In fact, the most effective check on the flow's movement seemed to be achieved by spraying about 150 ft (50 metres) from the front. This cooled the lava before it reached the front, but the effect of slowing the advance was not discernible until about a day later. The whole operation was apparently successful, for the lava piled up in ridges just short of the water and the harbour was saved. In fact, by the end of the eruption the harbour was better protected by the new lava than it had been previously.

Ten years later the attention of the world was focused on Mount Etna, where a new eruption down the south flank (the first down this side of the mountain for over seventy years) was destroying tourist facilities and farmland. Towards the end of April 1983, when the flow had destroyed four restaurants, a monastery and a large number of farms, homes, holiday chalets and ski lifts, the Italian government decided to finance an attempt to stop the flow to prevent further destruction.

Mount Etna is a gigantic aquifer through which rainwater percolates like a sieve, so there is no ready water supply in the form of streams or rivers for flow cooling. It was decided instead to create a diversion barrier and to bomb the flow, but in view of the precise positioning needed and the proximity to the still-surviving cable car pylons, aerial bombing would be unsuitable. To overcome this problem explosives were used on the ground instead.

The plan was to break open the frozen sides of the flow high up near the vent, making an easier path for the lava to flow down and creating a new flow beside the already existing one. Further down, an enormous earth wall was constructed. This would divert the new flow back on to the old one, where it would have to reconstruct a new lava field on top of the old, which had taken four weeks to spread this far. It was hoped that this would delay the advance of the flow front for at least a month, by which time the eruption might have slowed down or stopped.

The explosives were to be placed where the main lava channel neared the edge of the flow on the western side. Three rows of holes to receive the charges were drilled into the confining levee wall and water-cooling systems were placed inside these holes so that an explosion would not be prematurely triggered by the heat. Unfortunately, this cooling had the unforeseen effect of freezing the lava flowing inside, thickening the wall and narrowing the channel so that it overflowed. This resulted in the work area being flooded and the lowest (and most important) row of holes for the explosive charges being covered up. Despite this setback, it was decided to go ahead with the explosion at once. The levee wall was breached, a small stream of lava flowed out into the prepared channel, but it stopped after only a few hundred yards. The attempt was widely publicized by the waiting journalists as a failure, but they did not wait to see the after-effects of the explosion.

After unforeseen occurrence was the amount of cooler wall rock that was blown into the lava channel and carried downstream. This effectively blocked the entire channel a little lower down, causing the lava to overflow, by chance on the western side, exactly where it had been planned to go. It came up against the earth barrier and was diverted back on to the flow, but the volume of lava was so great that this barrier was soon overtopped and a larger one had to be built a little further to the west.

In the end, this unexpected circumstance caused the operation to continue more or less as planned. The flow did cease to advance, though this was some time after the explosion had taken place. As in all the diversion attempts previously described, there was considerable argument as to whether this one really had any significant effect on the overall damage caused by the eruption. Since it is not known what would have happened had nothing been done, these arguments will probably continue to be thrashed out in volcanological literature. Whether the diversion can be judged a success or not, the farmers and those who make their living from tourism on the south flank of Etna were delighted with the outcome. In particular, the Sapienza Hotel, which lies at the foot of the cable car, was saved by the earth barrier around it.

The Sapienza Hotel and other nearby tourist facilities were protected from the 1983 lava of Mount Etna by the construction of the huge protective barrier of earth on the left. Lava was also partially diverted with explosives.

Lava from Helgafell, Iceland, in 1973 was controlled, apparently successfully, by spraying thousands of gallons of water on to strategically important parts of the active flow. This cooled the flow down so that it did not travel so far.

Cross-sections of Kelut crater lake, Indonesia, and drainage tunnels before (top) and after (bottom) the 1951 eruption.

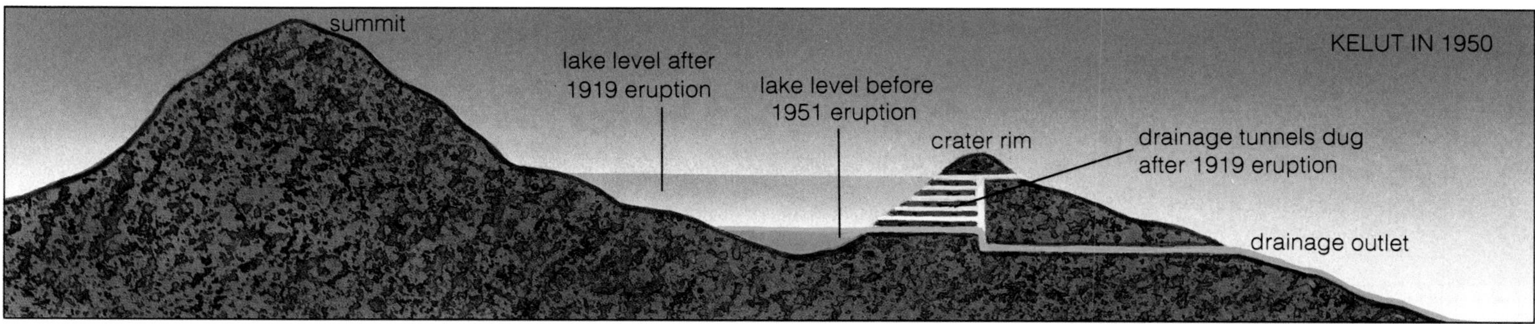

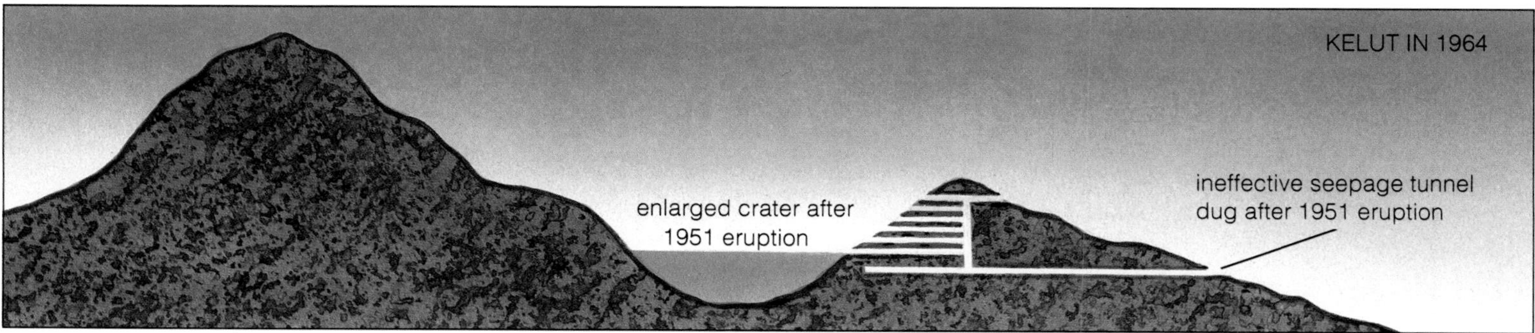

CONTROL OF CRATER LAKES

Crater lakes on active volcanoes may present a considerable danger. If the lake water is suddenly dislodged during an eruption, floods and lahars may come rushing down the volcano at great speed, causing more deaths than a lava flow because there is no time to get out of the way.

In Indonesia, where tropical rainfall and weathering can quickly produce impervious clays within volcanic craters, crater lakes are relatively common and the authorities have tried to limit the damage caused by them on several occasions. When the water in the crater lake is very acidic, as at Kawah Idjen in Java, the damage can be even worse. When this volcano erupted in 1817, the damage was so severe that the Dutch colonial engineers constructed a sluice at the lowest point on the crater rim so that the water would drain away and keep the level of the lake harmlessly low.

The most devastating of all these crater lake volcanoes is Kelut, also on Java. Kelut periodically ejects its crater lake during eruptions, which occur about every thirteen years on average. Deaths from lahars were therefore a regular occurrence and many attempts were made to control them. Dams were built across stream valleys and in 1905 a 10-ft (3-metre) wall was built across the most notorious valley to retain any future mudflows. This barrier was pitifully ineffective, for when the next big lahars were generated during the eruption of 1919, they swept straight over the wall and killed 5500 people further downslope.

The terrible effects of this eruption prompted the Dutch to tackle the problem more seriously, and it was decided that the most effective solution would be to drain away the crater lake, as had been done at Kawah Idjen. A drainage tunnel was dug just above the lake surface and water was syphoned out until the lake level had dropped by about 33 ft (10 metres). Another tunnel was then dug just above the lake surface and water was syphoned off until the level reduced a further 33 ft (10 metres). This process continued until the crater lake level was lowered by nearly 200 ft (60 metres), reducing the volume of water by 95 per cent.

This strategy worked well, and even the particularly violent eruption of 1951 killed only seven people, none of them by mudflows. However, it did damage the drainage system and also deepened the crater by 230 ft (70 metres). Although the lowest tunnel could be cleared, there were now 1400 million cubic ft (40 million cubic metres) of water because of the deepened lake, so another tunnel was constructed 65 ft (20 metres) lower. However, this tunnel was not extended to the lake itself as it was hoped that water would seep through and lower the lake gradually to the level of the tunnel. This did not happen, and in 1965 two Indonesians published a paper pointing out that the lake still contained a huge quantity of water, that it was fourteen years since the 1951 eruption, so another was likely soon, and that the displacement of so much water would be sufficient to create disastrous lahars.

A view of Poás crater and its lake.

Their predictions were proved perfectly correct. The next eruption came the following year, the crater lake was dislodged and several hundred people were killed by lahars. A new, lower tunnel was constructed in 1967, once more draining the lake to a safe level.

Strangely enough, precisely the opposite tactics have been proposed to mitigate the effects of Poás volcano in Costa Rica (see p. 133). The crater lake as Poás helps to stabilize short-term variations in heat output, cooling down the top of the magma column beneath the volcano sufficiently to keep it frozen and prevent eruptions. Recently, however, a small increase in thermal output from the magma has caused the lake to dry out completely during the dry season in both 1989 and 1990. This permitted small ash eruptions from the crater, which led to an increase in respiratory problems in the villages downwind of the volcano (see p. 166). It has been suggested that the construction of a channel from a higher lake nearby, the Laguna del Poás, would allow the level of the crater lake to be kept topped up and prevent it from drying out in the dry season. Such a move would keep respiratory problems down and also stabilize the activity.

This plan could work only on a short-term basis. If a major increase in heat output or magma input were to happen, the lake water would be insufficient to control it and an eruption would occur. However, lahars are not likely to be a problem at Poás, as the lake at its maximum has a volume of only 66 million cubic ft (2 million cubic metres).

These two examples show what can be done to mitigate problems in two specific cases. The drainage of crater lakes to put an end to the danger of lahars might be applied elsewhere, for lahars are one of the major killers in volcanic eruptions, but generally speaking there is little or nothing that can be done to stop a major eruption. The damping down of Poás may work in its present state of activity, but there is no foreseeable way of preventing or delaying a major eruption on any volcano. The forces involved are too powerful and occur at too great a depth and over too wide an area for volcanologists to influence events.

This vast scale of volcanic force is not always appreciated by the general public. After the Mount St Helens eruption in May 1980, when the enthusiasm of the local population for 'a really good display' had changed to anger at the thick ash which was ruining their crops, choking their animals and getting into every corner of their houses, some wanted to know why the air force did not simply fly over the volcano and 'nuke it'. The simple answer is that apart from the disastrous effects of radioactive fallout, a nuclear explosion does not release nearly so much energy as a large volcanic eruption. In addition, blowing the top off a volcano might have the opposite effect to that desired. A high-level magma chamber could be suddenly exposed, and the depressurization of the magma could lead to a sudden and highly dangerous pyroclastic eruption, or at least an increase in activity that might otherwise have been contained.

16 VOLCANOES AND HUMAN ACTIVITIES

THE DISADVANTAGES

Most volcanoes are safe to visit for most of the time and the majority remain safe to live on for a lifetime. It is sometimes difficult for those who live in countries unaffected by volcanic activity to understand why anyone should want to live on a volcano at all. But exactly the same arguments apply to living next to a river. Anyone who builds a house on a riverbank knows perfectly well that once every thousand years or so the house is going to be destroyed by a flood, but the chances of it happening during that person's occupation of the house are small enough to be negligible. Even on a continuously active volcano like Etna, the chances of someone's house being destroyed by a lava flow – on the lower slopes at least – are also about once every thousand years.

Immediate dangers

Volcanic bombs (see p. 44) are less dangerous than they look and tend only to affect volcanologists or tourists who climb to the summit to get a good view of the activity. Although being hit on the head by even a small lump of rock is usually fatal, in normal strombolian activity the bombs are widely dispersed, so the chances of being hit, even when you are within range, are fairly small. However, statistics are critical here and watching strombolian activity for hours on end increases your chances of being hit. Unfortunately, it has become a kind of tradition to climb Stromboli and spend the night under the stars on the crater edge. It is a beautiful and dramatic sight and safe for a few minutes, but the cumulative effect of hundreds of tourists spending several hours, often asleep, at the edge of the danger zone means that the chance of injury is dramatically increased. Indeed, tourists are killed all too often at Stromboli.

Lava, although a major danger to property, is very rarely a danger to life as most flows travel slowly,

Dangers from volcanic eruptions. Bombs are usually only dangerous to volcanologists or tourists who venture too close; most people have the instinct to keep clear of explosive activity.

Nuées ardentes and other types of pyroclastic flow are far more dangerous, as they are unexpected, can travel several miles in a few minutes and kill everything in their path.

A modern source of danger is the threat of ashfalls to aircraft. A thick ashfall may cause all engines on an aircraft to cut out at once, or may scratch and pit the windscreen so badly that it becomes impossible to see through.

giving plenty of time for people to get out of the way. A tragic exception was the eruption of Nyiragongo volcano in Zaire in 1977. There had been a very fluid lava lake inside this volcano for at least forty-two years, but after a series of earthquakes, cracks propagated within the volcano to the north and south and lava poured out almost like water. It raced down the mountain, destroying a village and killing all the inhabitants before they were aware of what was happening. This kind of event is extremely rare and few volcanoes have lava fluid enough to travel that fast.

The more usual danger familiar to volcanologists is of falling through the surface crust of a lava flow into the molten lava below. This, however, applies only to very fluid pahoehoe flows such as those on Hawaii or Iceland. It is often possible to walk (or rather run) over slow-moving aa flows, provided they are narrow enough, but the powerful smell of singed boots is often intolerable.

By far the most dangerous volcanic phenomenon is a pyroclastic flow (see p. 67). Ignimbrite eruptions are potentially the most lethal, but they are very rare, and the only known ignimbrite to have been formed this century (Mount Katmai, Alaska, 1912) was far enough away from population centres to cause no casualties. Much more common are the smaller nuées ardentes (see p. 15) associated with dome formation, such as those from Mount Pelée in Martinique. These kill simply because they travel very fast and are almost silent, so they give no warning.

Although a nuée may be quite powerful in the centre, capable of uprooting trees and destroying buildings, near the edges it may effectively be a hot wind. Near the edges of the Mount Pelée nuée of 8 May 1902 the heat was not sufficient to burn furnishings, so houses looked strangely untouched while everyone inside was killed. In these cases the heat was enough to scald the lungs; the scarred tissue could not take in oxygen, so victims actually died of suffocation.

Suffocation may also happen in a very thick ashfall (see p. 75), though it must be the right size and inhaled in great quantities before suffocation becomes a danger. This is what happened to the inhabitants of Pompeii during the AD 79 eruption of Vesuvius. Victims were buried under many feet of ash, but recent research on the position of their limbs suggests that heat and burns were also contributory factors.

A more modern problem from ashfalls is the danger to aircraft. While the scratching of a windscreen can pose a terrible hazard (see p. 122), a worse problem is engine failure due to choking by ash. On 14 December 1989 a plane carrying 245 people passed through an eruption cloud from Mount Redoubt, Alaska, and lost power in all its engines for eight minutes. Luckily, they eventually restarted and the plane landed safely.

Dangers from associated phenomena

Tsunamis (see p. 9), incorrectly called tidal waves (they have nothing to do with tides), are extremely destructive and dangerous, particularly as they come with little or no warning. They are usually associated with earthquakes, but the eruption of Krakatoa in 1883, which involved either caldera collapse or sector collapses, provoked giant tsunamis that caused the deaths of over 36,000 people up to 120 miles (200 km) away (see pp 9–11).

Much more commonly, death from volcanoes is caused by lahars (see p. 82). These may be caused by heavy rainfall, or by breaching or overflow of a summit crater lake (see p. 133). A similar effect may result from the heat of an eruption rapidly melting snow or ice, causing it to flood down the mountain, combining with ash on the way to form a speeding flow of mud. The most devastating example occurred at Nevado del Ruiz, Colombia, in 1985, causing the deaths of 22,000 people (see p. 122).

Lahars may also be caused by nuées ardentes rushing down stream valleys, piling up water ahead and incorporating it into the ash and pumice to make a fast-flowing hot mud. This type of effect certainly added to the lahars from Ruiz volcano, all of which came down stream valleys during heavy rain.

Unfortunately, lahars are a comparatively common occurrence on some volcanoes and are responsible for many deaths, albeit on a less spectacular but no less tragic scale than more headline-grabbing cataclysms. Even discounting the Ruiz disaster, lahars still accounted for over 300 deaths worldwide in the ten years between 1975 and 1985. The problem is that many small farmers set up home next to streams on volcanic ash, where the ready water supply and fertile soils are ideal for farming. Although the volcano may be many miles away, the lahars will always follow the valleys, so sooner or later such farms are likely to be hit. Lahars travel fast and comparatively silently, so they may arrive completely without warning. In 1877 a lahar from the upper slopes of Cotopaxi volcano in Ecuador hit a village 150 miles (240 km) away after travelling a total distance of 205 miles (320 km) along a circuitous valley.

Volcanic gas may also cause deaths from time to time, but some volcanoes cause milder though more persistent pernicious effects on the surrounding population. Poás volcano in Costa Rica, for example, causes respiratory problems at villages several miles downwind of the volcano. This volcano has a concentrated, acidic crater lake from which many gases are given off, including sulphur dioxide, hydrogen sulphide and hydrogen chloride. These also mix with the acids evaporated from the lake to form an unpleasant cocktail of gases and acid droplets. The size of the droplets is critical as to whether they can be inhaled and cause problems. During the dry season, when the lake dries up or becomes concentrated, the incidence of chest problems increases.

Some gases may kill outright. Hydrogen sulphide is lethal if it occurs in high enough concentrations, but much more common is carbon dioxide drowning. While not poisonous, carbon dioxide is heavier than air and on calm days it may collect in hollows. Unsuspecting people who wander into the hollows will breathe the pure gas and 'drown' from lack of oxygen. This occasionally happens in Hawaii, and also caused the deaths of more than 1700 people in Cameroon during August 1984 and 1986. In these cases the gas had apparently accumulated over a long period under sediments at the bottom of the crater lakes, but had all been dislodged at once. Neither crater has been active in historic time. In Java 149 people were killed in 1979 when Sinila Crater emitted a thick cloud of ash and gas, including hydrogen sulphide and carbon dioxide.

Logically, but none the less tragically, the greatest death tolls from volcanic eruptions have been caused by starvation in the aftermath of the devastation. The Laki Fissure eruption of 1783 produced so much ash that it formed a thick layer over much of Iceland. Vegetation was killed over a wide area near the eruption, but even further away it was too ashy to be eaten by grazing animals. Half the cattle and three-quarters of the sheep died of starvation, to be followed by the people who depended upon them for milk and meat. Turning to fish to sustain them, people found it impossible to put to sea as haze from the ash and gas severely reduced visibility.

Altogether 10,000 people, or about one fifth of the entire population of Iceland, died from the after-effects of this eruption. The even bigger and more explosive eruption of Tambora in 1815 directly killed about 12,000 people, but a further 70,000 died of starvation and disease over the following months.

Cars cut off and then surrounded by lava in Hawaii's East Rift zone.

The steamship Berouw *washed 1½ miles (2 km) inland by a gigantic tsunami wave associated with the Krakatoa eruption of 1883.*

Volcanoes will always attract farmers because volcanic soil is so fertile and easy to work.

THE ADVANTAGES

Given all the destruction and havoc that volcanoes can wreak, it may be thought surprising that they can actually have some positive attributes.

Agriculture

Fertile land is probably the main attraction that keeps countless millions of people living on or near volcanoes the world over. Soils derived from volcanic ashes, lavas and ignimbrites are well drained, have a high soil nutrient content, retain moisture well, have an excellent soil structure and are very light and easy to work. Even on well-established soils, the effect of a light ashfall is like the sprinkling of free fertilizer, as it adds fresh nutrients to the soil. Where the ashfall is so heavy that plants are destroyed, the improved crop yield in ensuing years may more than compensate.

The exact type of soil developed on a volcano depends upon the age and weathering of volcanic products, which in turn depend upon climate, but generally speaking, volcanic soils are capable of supporting a wide variety of crops. These include coffee on Central American volcanoes, vines and chestnut trees on Italian volcanoes and rice on Japanese volcanoes. Around the world volcanoes attract poor subsistence farmers who grow fruit and vegetables to feed their families and sell what surplus they can. This means that in countries such as Indonesia agricultural communities are always concentrated on active or recently active volcanoes.

Useful by-products

Many volcanic rocks make excellent building stone. For example, the city of Catania at the foot of Mount Etna shares with Edinburgh the fact that many of its buildings are constructed from basalt lavas from nearby volcanic centres. In Catania the streets are also paved with lava, but in Scotland and elsewhere in the British Isles granite is more commonly used, at least for kerbstones.

In some areas lightweight, honeycombed pumice, which has thermal insulation properties, is used as breezeblocks in buildings. However, it is probably more widely used in bathrooms and industry for its abrasive properties.

Building aggregate, gravel, cinders and sand are also freely available on volcanoes, and their use in concrete structures and road-building is evident all over the world. Even slate is metamorphosed volcanic rock.

Valuable by-products

Of greater economic importance are the concentrations of important or precious minerals that are found near volcanoes, or in association with past volcanic centres. The most spectacular of these is diamond. The most productive diamond mine in the world, at Kimberley in South Africa, lies in an old volcanic neck, the volcano above having been eroded away long ago. The present land surface is about 3300 ft (1000 metres) below the original surface, and the present mine has excavated a further 3300 ft (1000 metres) below ground into the pipe of the old volcano. Here the high temperatures and pressures associated with the intrusion of magma have produced enormous quantities of diamonds.

Precious and commercially important metals, including gold, silver, copper, lead, uranium and tin, may all be concentrated by volcanic action. Where magmas are rich in these elements, bodies of ores may occur near the surface in high enough concentrations for them to be commercially viable. Cripple Creek gold mines in the USA, Cerro Rico silver mine in Bolivia, and El Teniente copper mine in Chile are all examples of high concentrations of precious metals in old volcanic pipes. Other rare elements, minerals and gems are also found in igneous rocks.

Active volcanoes are mined for sulphur in many places, including Chile, Sicily and Mexico. There was even a sulphur mine inside Vulcano crater before the 1888 eruption. In addition, commercially important substances are found in volcanic lakes or steam. The discovery of boric acid in natural steam vents and pools in Italy in 1777 meant that expensive imports of borax could be abandoned in favour of the locally extracted product. Borax is now also mined on volcanoes in Chile and elsewhere.

Geothermal power

With the ever-increasing world demand for energy, plus a growing awareness of radiation hazards from nuclear power stations and pollution from conventional ones, geothermal power is rapidly emerging as one of the most important and, so far, least developed sources of clean world energy. Italy was the first country to realize the enormous potential to be derived from the gigantic and long-lasting power output of a volcano. During the nineteenth century, in the Larderello area, south of Florence, heat from natural steam vents was used in the chemical industry and to heat the boilers of a steam engine. In 1904 it was also used to

Sulphur mine at Aucanquilcha volcano, northern Chile. Loaded trucks have to negotiate the hazardous zigzag road from the top.

drive a dynamo that provided electric light for the chemical works. This was the world's first geothermal generator.

From this modest beginning electricity generation was steadily increased, new techniques were tested and introduced, and Lardarello now produces a major part of Italy's electricity supply. Other countries have been slow to follow; New Zealand began to produce geothermal power at Wairikei in 1958, and the USA, Japan, Iceland and the USSR followed in the 1960s. Today geothermal projects are going ahead all over the world and they promise to be particularly important to Third World countries, where lack of raw materials and the high cost of importation forbids the use of coal, oil or nuclear power.

Tourism

With the advent of cheap air fares and the consequent mobility of the modern tourist, active volcanoes are becoming steadily more important as tourist attractions. Although the inhabitants of Nicolosi on Mount Etna, for example, have been making a living as volcano guides since the eighteenth century, tourism has boomed only since the 1950s. Currently, it is not uncommon for several thousand people a day to visit the volcano at the height of the season. There are now two companies running regular trips to the summit, dozens of shops, hotels and restaurants, and hundreds of companies producing souvenirs and other goods which depend upon tourism for their existence.

A similar increase in tourism at places much further afield, such as Indonesia, the Philippines and Central and South America, has meant that similar operations have become commercially viable at volcanoes here as well, and many tour companies today include visits to an active volcano as part of their package.

Even when volcanoes have ceased to be active, they can still attract visitors and income because of the magnificent scenery they create. Some of the most popular national parks in America, including Yellowstone Park, Lassen Peak, Crater Lake Oregon, as well as the rather more obvious Valley of Ten Thousand Smokes, are all recent or still active volcanic areas. In both France and Germany spa towns and health resorts still attract enormous numbers of visitors; the towns of Royat and Chamalières, for example, in the Auvergne have grown up around the hot springs associated with the volcanism of the Chaîne des Puys, which last erupted about 5000 years ago.

Geothermal power is becoming an increasingly important source of energy in volcanic areas.

17 VOLCANOES IN THE SOLAR SYSTEM

VOLCANIC AND IMPACT CRATERS ON THE MOON

One of the longest-lasting scientific controversies of all time was over the origin of craters on the Moon. It was in the middle of the seventeenth century that scientist Robert Hooke first suggested that they might be due to the impact of large objects crashing in the Moon, but since meteorites and asteroids were then unknown, no one took the idea seriously. For centuries the great weight of opinion was in favour of a volcanic origin for lunar craters and this persisted until after the two world wars. It was only then that the strong resemblance between bomb craters and lunar craters was noted, together with the clear difference in shape between lunar craters and volcanoes. Consequently, more and more astronomers began to look at the impact theory with increased interest.

The controversy continued to rage until well after the first manned lunar landings, for the evidence brought back from the lunar rocks was still ambiguous. Nowadays we know that both types of crater occur on the Moon, but the consensus of opinion is that the great majority of craters on the Moon, including virtually all those visible through telescopes from Earth, are of impact origin, caused by huge masses of rock crashing into the Moon during the final stages of planetary accretion 4000 million years ago. Since that time there have been fewer and fewer impacts, as most of the objects capable of hitting the Moon would have done so relatively early in its history. The most recent impact craters stand out as bright and fresh-looking, but even these 'youngsters' are old by Earth standards. The crater Aristarchus, for example, 25 miles (40 km) across and one of the youngest of the large lunar craters, is Triassic in age, i.e. more than 200 million years old.

In the years immediately following the first close-up spacecraft pictures and the manned lunar landings in the 1960s and early 1970s there were problems in interpreting some of the fascinating discoveries that were made. In the first place, it became increasingly clear that the large craters were of impact origin, yet at the same time it was obvious from chemical and mineralogical analysis that the vast, flat plains of dust and rocks, called *maria*, were composed of very old basaltic lava, the last of it erupted more than 2000 million years ago. Again, this is young compared with the age of most of the impact craters and these eruptions represent one of the last geological events on the Moon. These vast marial plains are enormous – thousands of miles wide in some cases – and the individual lavas in them must be of much larger volume than any so far discovered on Earth. Yet if this is basaltic lava produced on such a gigantic scale, where are the vast craters from which it was erupted and the flow fronts which mark the edges of the vast individual flows?

This last question was answered fairly soon. Although the *Orbiter* and *Apollo* craft photographed some clearly-defined flow fronts in the Mare Imbrium, these were exceptional. At the same time, experiments on lavas of lunar composition showed that they were ten times less viscous than any known lavas on Earth. Most lunar lavas therefore flowed very far, very fast, filling hollows like water and leaving no flow fronts at all. But where are the lunar volcanoes?

LUNAR VOLCANOES

Although comparatively rare and very small in comparison with the huge impact craters all around them, lunar volcanoes are large compared with volcanic craters on Earth. They divide into two categories: collapse craters and pyroclastic cones.

Collapse craters are found up to a few miles across and these are recognizable by their non-circular shape, their steep, cliff-like inner walls and the very shallow or non-existent outer slopes. In many cases they closely resemble calderas on Earth.

The craters of *pyroclastic cones* are smaller – usually less than ½ mile (1 km) in diameter – though this is also about the maximum diameter for such craters on Earth. The gravity on the Moon is about one sixth of that on the Earth, however, so pyroclastic material will be thrown six times as far on the Moon. They tend to cluster in specific areas, along with other types of volcanic features, and are often elongated and associated with visible fractures.

There are some characteristic types of lunar volcanoes that have no exact equivalent on Earth. The earliest of these to be discovered were the *lunar domes*, a confusing term as they are completely different in appearance from volcanic domes on Earth. They consist of circular swellings up to about 12 miles (20 km) across, often with a crater at the top, but with extremely shallow slopes of never more than a few degrees, so they are visible only under low illumination. In some respects they resemble the shallow shield volcanoes of Hawaii. Steeper lava domes are also found, mainly concentrated in one area – the Marius Hills – and these consist of much more irregular and steeper swellings, apparently formed by small eruptions of more viscous and perhaps more differentiated lava.

Although interesting, none of the lunar volcanoes mentioned so far show any evidence of being the source of the huge lavas that make up the lunar maria. However, there is one curious type of lunar feature that remained an enigma for a long time. There are many examples of faults, fissures and downfaulted valleys on the Moon, collectively known as *rilles*, as they were originally thought to be streams. However, a special group called *sinuous rilles* is distinctly different from the others. These rilles curve and meander about just like riverbeds and there were many who regarded them as old watercourses right up until the lunar landings. But there are distinct differences. Sinuous rilles are much bigger, being up to 2½ miles (4 km) wide and over 65 miles (200 km) long. They also usually begin in a caldera and instead of widening downstream like rivers, they get narrower and shallower until they are no longer detectable. After *Apollo 15* landed next to one of them (Hadley Rille), it became clear that sinuous rilles are actually vast lava channels, similar to those that occur in basaltic lavas on Earth, but formed in the much more fluid and voluminous lavas of the Moon.

From their distribution around the edges of the lava plains of the maria, it is clear that the sinuous rilles, or rather the calderas at their head, were the prolific volcanoes that fed these huge marial lava flows. Their comparatively insignificant appearance lies in the extremely low viscosity of the lunar lavas, for although

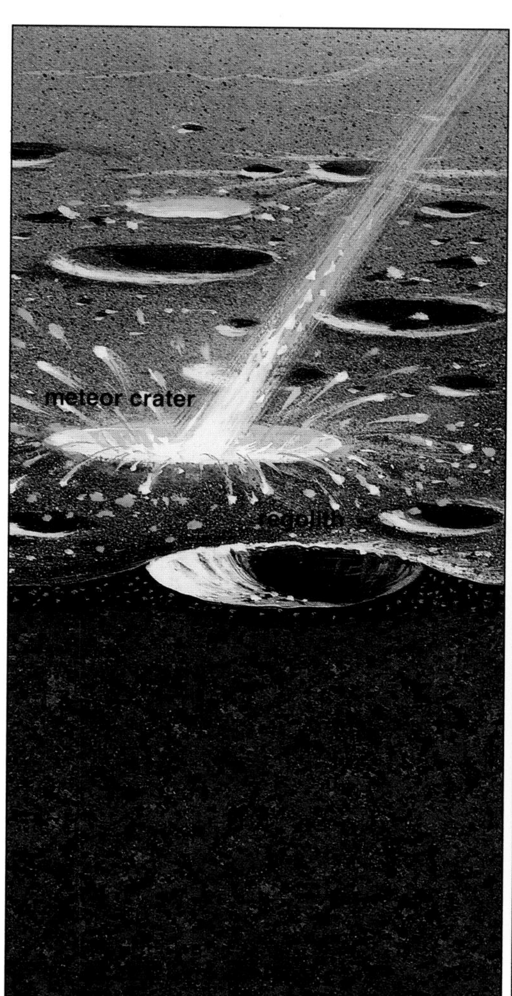

Regardless of the angle at which an impacting body strikes the surface of the Moon, it produces a circular crater.

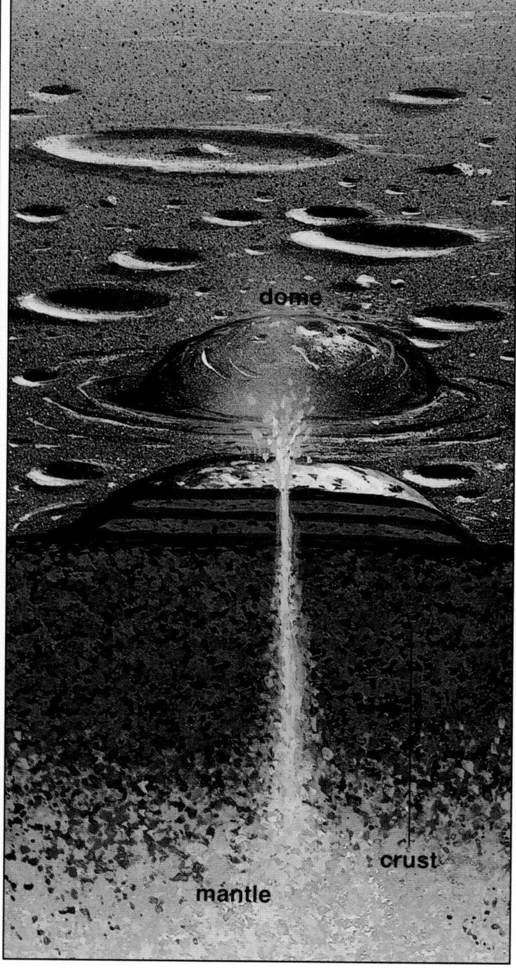

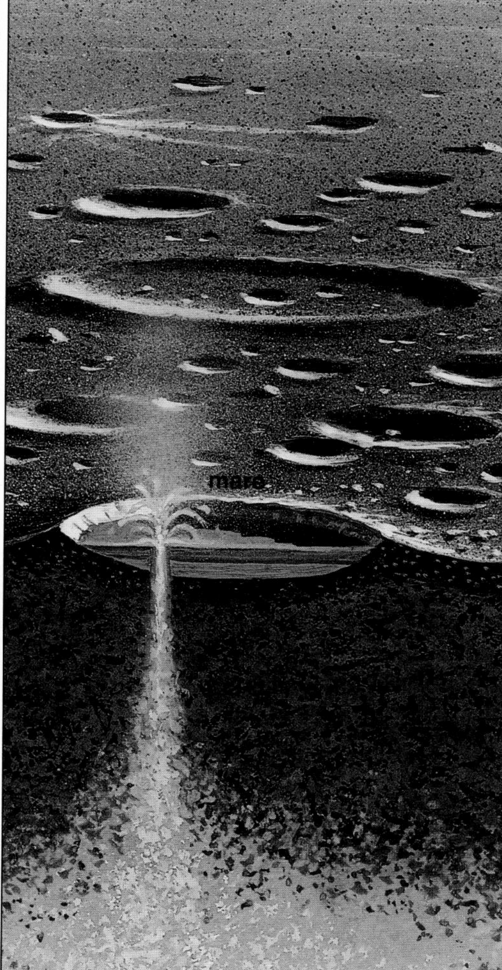

Large volumes of basalt lava flooded some areas of the Moon 3–4 thousand million years ago. Where the lava was slightly more viscous, lunar domes were formed. Some impact craters were later flooded by lava to create a flat floor.

Map of Olympus Mons, Mars, the largest volcano in the solar system, and three volcanoes of the Tharsis ridge, all of which are about 17 miles (27 km) high.

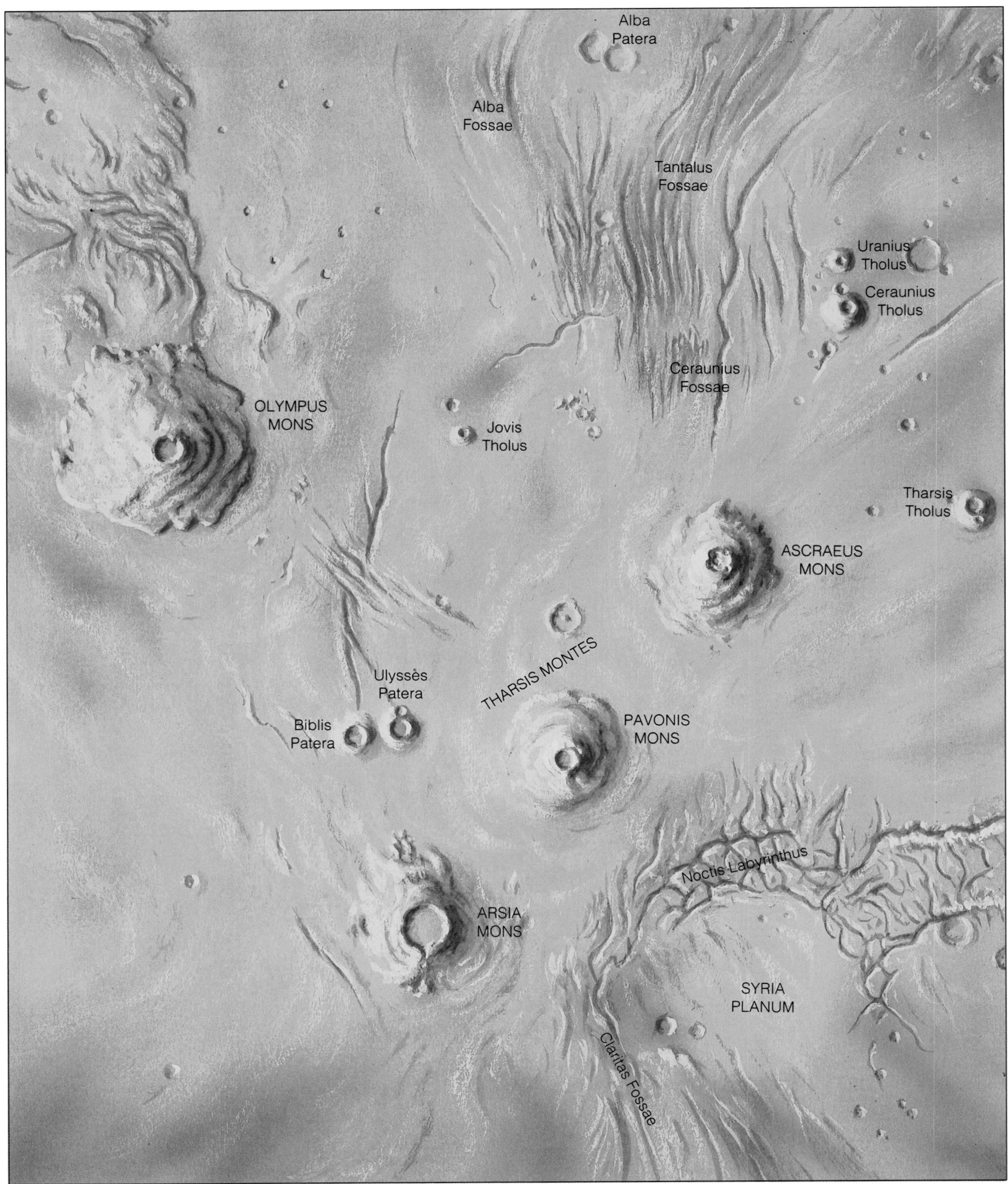

OVERLEAF: The northern Tharsis area of Mars, looking across the smaller Uranius Tholus volcano to Ceraunius Tholus, which measures about 68 × 56 miles (110 × 90 km).

these eruptions may have lasted for years and been of the most enormous volume, they were never able to build up a respectable-looking volcano; the lavas were just too fluid, running for hundreds of miles and filling hollows, rather than building up tall volcanoes as would the more viscous lavas of Earth.

This great age of lava eruption on the Moon lasted from about 3900 to just over 2000 million years before the present, after which the entire Moon became extinct, with only the smallest of partially molten cores now remaining at the centre.

VOLCANOES ON MARS

Mars has long held the popular imagination as a possible abode of intelligent life and as a rival to Venice or Amsterdam, but nowhere in the various imagined escapades of space travellers, or even in the serious scientific writings of planetary astronomers, did volcanoes play a large part. It was therefore a complete surprise when, after three previous spacecraft to Mars had somehow avoided all the interesting areas, *Mariner 9* in 1971 began to photograph huge volcanoes.

The Tharsis area, where white clouds often appeared and which had a tiny white spot nearby, had been seen since the nineteenth century through telescopes from Earth. The name of the white spot – Nix Olympica (the snows of Olympus) – even suggested that it might be a mountain, but what *Mariner 9* photographed was a volcano over 17 miles (27 km) high and 300 miles (500 km) across. Renamed Olympus Mons, this is by far the largest volcano in the entire solar system, and three volcanoes nearby – Ascraeus Mons, Pavonis Mons and Arsia Mons on the Tharsis ridge – are all 17 miles (27 km) high. The Hawaiian volcano Mauna Loa, the largest on Earth, even when measured from its base on the sea floor, is only 6 miles (10 km) high and 120 miles (195 km) wide, with a volume at least twenty times smaller than Olympus Mons. The latter may at one time have been even wider, for it is surrounded on all sides by cliffs up to 2 miles (3 km) high, apparently the scars of huge landslides that removed much of the lower slopes.

In contrast to the Moon, the volcanoes of Mars resemble those of the Earth in many characteristics, apart from their great size. The hundreds of individual lava flows which make up their steep slopes are plainly visible descending from the summit calderas, which resemble those of shield volcanoes on Earth, except that they too are much bigger – 45 miles (70 km) across in the case of Olympus Mons. Smaller volcanoes do exist, however; in the Elysium region the highest volcanoes are only 7½ miles (12 km) high, and in both Tharsis and Elysium there are some lower than ½ mile (1 km) in height, though the craters are still large compared to those on Earth. Unfortunately, all volcanoes on Mars, like those of the Moon, have long since been extinct and the impact craters on them suggest that they have been so for at least some hundreds of millions of years.

So how did Mars, a planet little more than half the diameter of Earth, come to have such gigantic volcanoes? Part of the answer may be provided by examining why volcanoes on Earth never grow so big. The highest volcanoes on Earth rise to 4 miles (6 km) above sea level and it has been suggested that they cannot grow any higher because the Earth's lithosphere (crust) is too thin. The weight of the lithosphere may squeeze regions of magma generation beneath, providing part of the force extruding lavas. The lithosphere of Mars was much thicker, thus providing a much greater hydrostatic head which allowed lavas to be erupted at much greater heights and volcanoes to grow much higher. It has been suggested that 17 miles (27 km) is the upper limit for volcano height on Mars; above this the magma pressure is never sufficiently great to produce an eruption. This would explain why the four largest volcanoes all have the same altitude.

Earth's volcanoes are strongly controlled by plate movements, but on Mars, as on the Moon, it is clear that there has never been a system of plate tectonics or continental drift. One of the reasons that volcanoes over mantle plumes or 'hot spots' such as Hawaii never grow any bigger is that the moving plate carries them away from the hot spot, so after a certain period the volcanoes, deprived of magma supply, become extinct. Since on Mars there is no plate movement, it may be that such mantle plumes can continue to supply magma to volcanoes indefinitely, or at least until they reach the height of the hydrostatic head.

Apart from such spectacular volcanoes and the huge lava flows emitted from them, sometimes for hundreds of miles, Mars also has evidence of extensive past tectonic activity, with thousands of large faults, cracks and fissures. The largest of these is the Valles Marineris, a vast rift valley (again the largest in the solar system), over 2½ miles (4 km) deep in places, up to 180 miles (300 km) wide and more than 2500 miles (4000 km) long. As well as being a valley, it also lies at the top of a broad, shallow ridge, 6 miles (10 km) high

Volcanoes on Venus: a scene based on recent radar images from the Magellan *probe.*

at its highest point. The whole system is reminiscent of a gigantic mid-ocean ridge and it is just possible that it is some kind of incipient spreading axis, like the East African Rift, lying over an ancient rising convection current within the Martian mantle. This would have raised the surface and split it as the two sides moved apart, but with no corresponding subduction zone, perhaps because the thicker Martian lithosphere required great energy to buckle, a true plate tectonic system never got under way.

VOLCANOES ON VENUS

Venus is the planet that comes closest to the Earth, sometimes a mere 25 million miles (39 million km) from us (as opposed to 35 million miles (60 million km) for Mars's closest approach). Despite this proximity, it has always been one of the least known of all the planets. One problem is that being nearer to the Sun, it always presents its dark, unilluminated face to us when at its closest. Another problem is that its atmosphere of mainly carbon dioxide is always so thick that the surface can never be seen from Earth; this atmosphere is also so bright and featureless that cloud movements cannot be followed, except in ultraviolet light. This inaccessibility meant that even the rotation period of the planet was unknown until 1965, when the results of long-term radar observations began to bear fruit.

Spacecraft investigation of Venus has been similarly difficult. The Russian spacecraft that visited the planet in the 1960s were built to withstand the high pressures expected from the thick atmosphere, but each one lasted until the huge pressures had been reached and was then crushed. It was not until 1970 that a spacecraft finally managed to touch down intact. The surface pressure was found to be ninety times greater than on Earth, but worse still, the clouds of Venus are thought to be made up of sulphuric acid; this may combine with fluorine in the atmosphere to form fluorosulphuric acid, a very corrosive compound. This could explain why it was not until 1975 that two spacecraft lasted long enough to send back pictures of the surface, but even they did so for only an hour.

In view of the corrosive atmosphere, a highly eroded surface had been expected, so it was rather surprising that the surface pictures showed comparatively freshly broken rocks, which suggests that the planet is still geologically and perhaps volcanically active. This conclusion was confirmed by more detailed radar mapping of the surface in the 1970s and 1980s from both Earth-based and spacecraft instruments, most recently those of the *Magellan* craft. These radar maps show vast areas of both high and low land, together with many volcanic edifices and craters. The high and low areas are suggestive of continental and sea floor topography on Earth and it was thought possible that a plate tectonic system similar to Earth's operates there now. The recent images from *Magellan* do not support this view (see p. 186). However, many different types of volcano, including large domes of apparently evolved lava, have been discovered. The exciting possibility that Venus still has active volcanoes remains to be confirmed as the plume from an active volcano would not show on a radar image, but again, this would not be surprising.

One of the greatest surprises from the exploration of space came late – nearly twenty years after man's first flight into space. The first few years of exploration had been somewhat disappointing as far as volcanoes went; the small, long-extinct volcanic craters of the Moon were not recognized at once, and although large volcanoes were found on Mars, these too became extinct long ago. Since 'the smaller the planet, the sooner it will cool down' was a good rule of thumb, Jupiter's satellites, similar to the Moon in size, seemed to be the last place to expect to find active volcanoes.

IO'S SULPHUR VOLCANOES

Great discoveries are often made in unspectacular ways. When the first pictures of Jupiter's satellite Io began to arrive at the Jet Propulsion Laboratory from the NASA *Voyager 1* spacecraft in March 1979, nothing unusual was noticed. The first intimation that something was wrong came when engineer Linda Morabito began routine image-scanning of the edge of Io to help fix the spacecraft's position. The computer repeatedly refused the data, but since some data is always lost in transmitting the pictures over the 500 million miles (800 million km) that separate Jupiter and the Earth, it was at first assumed that the odd values were transmission faults.

When the data was made into a picture, however, a strange pattern of bright material was seen above the surface of Io and it soon became clear that the brightness was caused by material being thrown out of a violently explosive volcano. In the following days eight further erupting volcanoes were found on Io, all of them explosive, with matter being ejected at very high speeds – up to ½ mile (1 km) per second – and

BELOW: A big surprise in the exploration of the solar system was the discovery in 1979 of very powerful active sulphur volcanoes on Jupiter's satellite Io, which spray fountains of pyroclastic material 60–250 miles (100–400 km) high.

OVERLEAF: Jupiter, seen as a crescent from a point above its highly volcanic satellite Io. (Painting from the private collection of Mrs B. Evans)

reaching heights of 30–220 miles (50–350 km). A large number of dormant volcanoes were also discovered.

Although these spectacular erupting volcanoes came as a dramatic surprise to most of the scientific community, the reasons for this unexpected activity had in fact been worked out and explained already. Three American scientists had been studying the orbit of Io around Jupiter. The gravitational attraction of the other satellites of Jupiter make Io's distance from Jupiter vary from day to day and it was found that this variation in distance was sufficient to cause quite significant changes in Io's shape. When closest to Jupiter, the enormous gravitational attraction of this planet (which is 300 times more massive than the Earth) raises huge tides in Io's solid surface of up to 330 ft (100 metres). These great changes in shape cause friction and consequent heating of the interior which has been sufficient to melt most of Io and produce large and unusual volcanoes on its surface. In an elegant demonstration of scientific method, the prediction of active volcanoes on Io was finally published on 2 March 1979, just two days before *Voyager 1* recorded the first signs of active volcanism outside the Earth.

The eruptions on Io are different from those on the Earth in many ways. Although violent ejection of material has been observed in phreatic (steam-blast) eruptions on Earth, terrestrial eruptions of this violence last only a few minutes at most. Not only were the eruptions on Io seen to continue for hours during the *Voyager 1* encounter, but when *Voyager 2* arrived at Jupiter four months later, eight of the eruptions seen by *Voyager 1* were still going strong.

Another peculiarity of Io's volcanoes is that they are composed largely of sulphur or sulphur compounds. It is also probable that sulphur, a volatile element, is responsible for providing the great driving force that produces the high ejection velocities. No active lava flows were detected during either of the *Voyager* encounters, but many recent flows were seen radiating from the active and inactive craters, and their colour and other characteristics suggest that these too are composed of molten sulphur.

18

THE FUTURE

In August 1989 at least two geyser-like plumes were discovered on Triton, Neptune's largest moon, by the *Voyager 2* spacecraft. The plumes were both dark, about 5 miles (8 km) high and rose from two of a number of dark spots near the planet's south pole. They appear to be caused by gas venting at the surface, carrying fine dark particles aloft. Although it is possible that these geyser-like features are driven by solar rather than geothermal heating, it underlines the fact that fundamental discoveries are still being made about volcanism on other bodies in the solar system.

At the time of writing, the *Magellan* spacecraft has just entered orbit around Venus and is sending back the first radar images, which show an extraordinary array of previously undetected features. Tectonic activity is clearly widespread and recent. Huge areas are covered with thousands upon thousands of parallel cracks, very narrow but stretching for hundreds of miles. Some of them form huge rings, suggesting updoming or downwarping on a large scale, but so far there are no signs of subduction zones. However, a great many much smaller volcanoes can be seen in clusters in many areas, looking no different from similar-sized volcanoes on Earth. Some of these may well be active.

Despite these exciting discoveries, and the many important ones that are still likely to be made on other planets and their satellites, there is no doubt that the main advances in volcanology in the future will be made here on Earth. One of the most immediate tasks to be carried out has nothing to do with understanding volcanoes in any academic way. The most pressing need at the moment is the proper monitoring of active volcanoes, particularly those which are close to large towns and areas of high population density.

Only a handful of volcanoes are now well enough understood for reasonable predictions about their activity to be made, and we still know very little at all about most volcanoes in the world. One of the results of the intensive study of the small number of well-observed volcanoes is that even those which appear to be of approximately the same type, such as Etna,

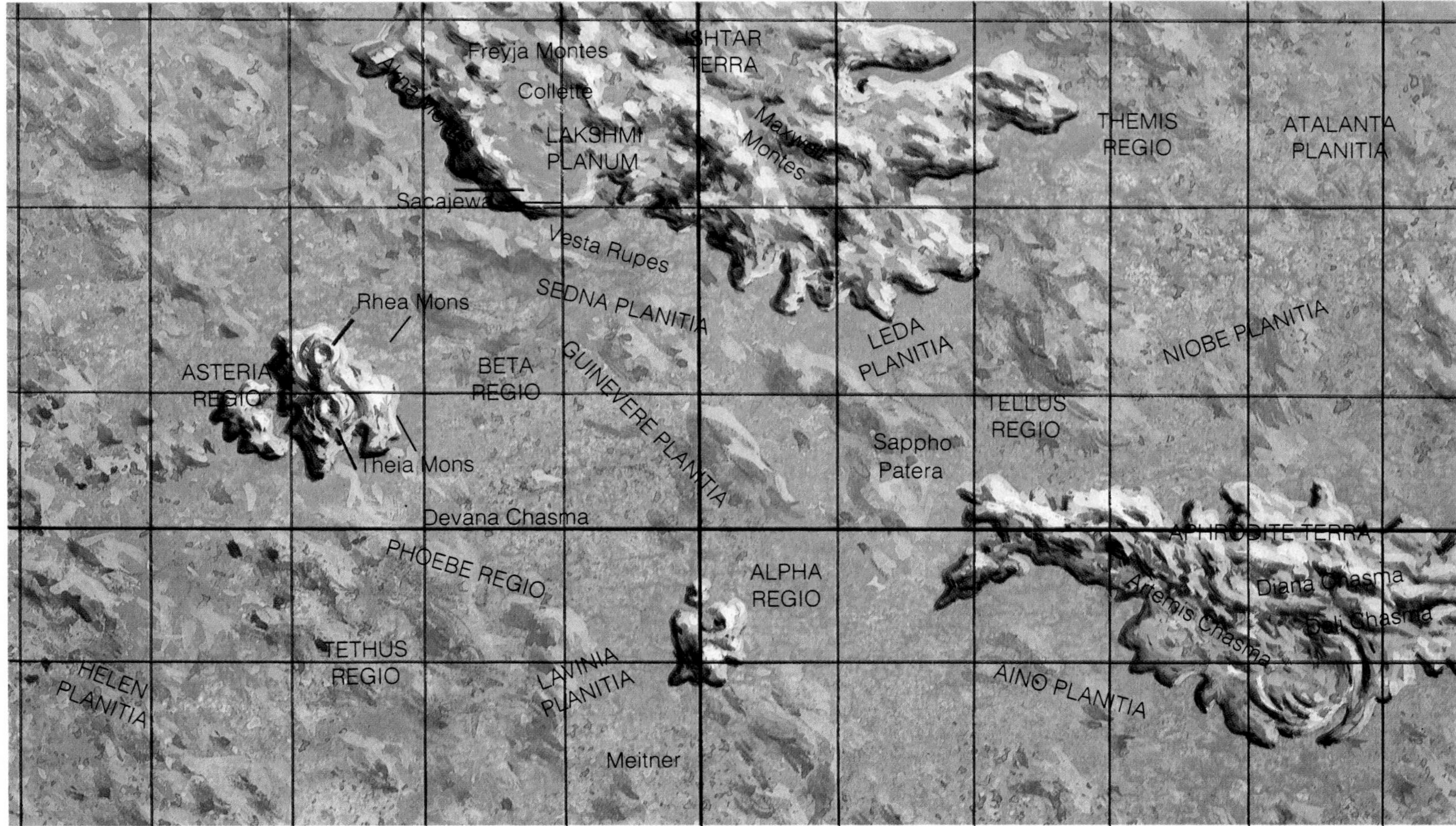

A map of the surface of Venus. Many of the mountainous areas have large volcanoes in them.

Kilauea and Piton de la Fournaise, have very different internal structures and eruptive mechanisms. This means that we cannot predict how one volcano will behave by assuming it to be similar to others. Each volcano is different from the next and has its own peculiar characteristics which can only be discovered and understood by comprehensive and permanent monitoring.

The need for such monitoring has recently been emphasized by two tragic events that occurred when this book was being completed. On June 1991 a pyroclastic flow poured down the side of Unzen volcano, Japan, killing 41 people, and then on 15 and 16 June strong explosions generated a series of huge pyroclastic flows from Mount Pinatubo in the Philippines, which killed more than 300.

Mount Unzen, like most of Japan, is an area that is well monitored, so when earthquakes were detected there in November 1990, funds were immediately made available by the Japanese government to set up ground deformation and seismometer networks. This meant that activity could be predicted accurately and evacuation carried out in time. Those killed were mainly volcanologists, press reporters, and members of the police and rescue services. Pyroclastic flows had already occurred from 24 May onwards, so all those killed were well aware of the dangers. The Philippines are not so well monitored, but volcanologists there made an excellent series of decisions with limited information, and probably saved well over 100,000 lives (see p. 157).

The full capacity for devastation of a volcanic eruption has yet to be seen in the modern world. Although terrible disasters have occurred, the greatest direct death toll (not counting famine) known in a volcanic eruption is 36,417 during the Krakatoa eruption of 1883. Although terrible enough, this is only the population of a fairly modest-sized town today. We have yet to see the effects of a nuée ardente on a modern city or, worse still, an ignimbrite eruption. If a major ignimbrite eruption were to occur in Japan, or in New Zealand or California, as is quite possible in the immediate future, then we might be counting the dead in millions rather than tens of thousands, and looking at the destruction of a nation's economy and a serious destabilization of world power rather than the loss of a few billion pounds. Approximately fifteen of the world's capital cities are in a position to be wiped out or seriously damaged by volcanic eruptions.

The secondary effects of a large volcanic eruption can be just as devastating. The largest tsunami known was one caused by a landslide which hit the sea in a remote bay in Alaska in 1958. Some 90 million tons of rock were involved in the slide and a gigantic wave rushed across the bay, racing nearly ⅓ mile (520 metres) up the hills opposite. When a sector collapse like that at Mount St Helens occurs in a volcano next to the sea, huge tsunamis are created. Many volcanoes, such as Etna and Vesuvius, are fairly close to the sea and sector collapse has occurred at both of them during the last few thousand years. Were such an event to occur again, the death toll from tsunamis around the Mediterranean shores could be appalling, particularly if such an event were to happen on a summer day when the beaches are crowded. A similar event occurred in association with Mount Unzen's last eruption in 1792. Some 15,000 people died when a dome collapsed near the summit and swept into the sea, causing a vast tsunami.

It is perhaps lack of awareness of these possibilities that accounts for the failure of many governments to take volcanoes seriously. As long as they are regarded as peripheral to the essential workings of a nation, the occasional tragedies that occur are unlikely to push authorities into a long-term commitment to finance volcano surveillance and planning for eventualities. It was the enormous cost of the unnecessary evacuation of 72,000 people on the French island of Guadaloupe in the Caribbean (see p. 145) that prompted the French government to finance research and proper surveillance of all active volcanoes in their territories, not just La Soufrière de Guadaloupe. It was largely as a result of this episode that an observatory was set up at Piton de la Fournaise volcano, on Réunion Island in the Indian Ocean, now one of the best observatories in the world and contributing to volcanological research as well as effecting basic surveillance.

On a more positive note, volcanoes can be exploited to great financial advantage (see pp 169–71). It is vital that more resources are committed to proper programmes of volcano study so that even greater advantage of them can be taken and appropriate defensive measures and precautions set in motion. Only then can we reap their full benefit while suffering the minimum inconvenience from their enormous power.

OVERLEAF: *In August 1989 the* Voyager 2 *probe sent back images of dark streaks in the southern area of Neptune's large moon Triton. These may be exotic types of geyser sending plumes of nitrogen gas several miles into the thin atmosphere. (Painting from the private collection of Mr P. Stark)*

HARDY
'89

INDEX

(Figures in *italics* indicate illustrations.)